English ꞁor the
Energy
Industry

EXPRESS SERIES

Simon Campbell

UNIVERSITY PRESS

OXFORD
UNIVERSITY PRESS

Great Clarendon Street, Oxford OX2 6DP

Oxford University Press is a department of the University of Oxford.
It furthers the University's objective of excellence in research, scholarship,
and education by publishing worldwide in

Oxford New York

Auckland Cape Town Dar es Salaam Hong Kong Karachi
Kuala Lumpur Madrid Melbourne Mexico City Nairobi
New Delhi Shanghai Taipei Toronto

With offices in

Argentina Austria Brazil Chile Czech Republic France Greece
Guatemala Hungary Italy Japan Poland Portugal Singapore
South Korea Switzerland Thailand Turkey Ukraine Vietnam

OXFORD and OXFORD ENGLISH are registered trade marks of
Oxford University Press in the UK and in certain other countries

© Oxford University Press 2009

Adapted from *English for the Energy Industry* by Simon Campbell
© Cornelsen Verlag GmbH & Co. OHG, Berlin 2008

The moral rights of the author have been asserted

Database right Oxford University Press (maker)

First published 2009

2013 2012 2011 2010 2009
10 9 8 7 6 5 4 3 2 1

ISBN: 978 0 19 457922 3

Printed in China

ACKNOWLEDGEMENTS

*The publisher would like to thank the following for their kind permission to
reproduce photographs and other copyright material*: istock pp 5 (power
station/Michael Utech), 6 (wind turbines/Joe McDaniel) , 9 (pylon/
Stewart Charles), 10 (business team, top/Michael DeLeon), 11 (smart
metre/Trevor Fisher), 13 (oil flame), 15 (car robot, top/Ricardo Azoury),
(meeting, bottom/Izvorinka Jankovic), 20 (computer user, left/Chris
Schmidt), (businesswoman, right/Willie B. Thomas) 22 (chimneys),
25 (flood/Chris Bolton), 26 (businesswoman), 29 (polar bear/Jan Will),
30 (nuclear power station/Rolf Fischer), 33 (warning sign, top/Evra
Serrabassa), (meeting, bottom/Mihai Calin) 41 (man, top left/Chris
Schmidt), (girl, top right/Red Dot Studio), (girl, middle left/Lisa Gagne),
(man, middle right/Arthur Kwialkowski), (man, bottom left/Jacob
Wackerhausen), (woman, bottom right/Jeffrey Smith), 43 (man on phone/
Paul Paladin), 50 (handshake/Carmen Martinez Banús), 51 (lecture/Luka
Esenko); Library of Congress, Prints & Photographs Division, p10 (Thomas
Edison [reproduction number, LC-USZ62-105139], bottom); Shutterstock
pp 31 (mine/Lee Prince), 39 (handshake, top/Stephen Coburn), (interview,
bottom/Bruce C. Murray); Starfish p 47 (geothermal house); Webstock
pp 34 (nuclear power station), 36 (nuclear power station workers).

Cartoons by: Stephen May

Cover images courtesy of: Jupiter Images (main image/Eric Millette/
Workbook Stock), Alamy Images (top left/Horizon International Images
Ltd), Getty Images (bottom left/Hank Morgan/Rainbow/Science Faction).

Diagrams by: Starfish Design, Editorial and Project Management

Contents

About the book

English for the Energy Industry is for people who need to communicate effectively in the energy business and its associated fields. The book will equip learners with the necessary linguistic skills to understand and talk about daily situations in the work environment and the more complex developments within the global energy market.

English for the Energy Industry is divided into six units and each unit has its own thematic focus. Each topic is relevant to employees engaged in different positions and roles: energy production and distribution, environmental protection, technology, sales and distribution, PR, business policy and strategy. The units are independent of each other so you can choose those that are more relevant to your area of expertise, or you can work through the units in sequence. It is, however, recommended that you start with Unit 1 as this provides an overview of the various topics.

Every unit begins with a **Starter** to introduce the topic. This is followed by dialogues, reading texts, diagrams, and authentic documents, as well as a variety of exercises designed to aid the learning of important vocabulary and phrases in contextual situations. In each unit you will be referred to the **Partner Files** at the back of the book. These are role-plays which enable learners to practise the vocabulary and language of the unit in realistic situations. The units end with **Output** activities, which consist of reading texts to extend the unit topic or offer further useful tips, and they also provide opportunities for discussion. When you have finished all the units, you can **Test yourself!** with a fun crossword at the back of the book.

At the back of **English for the Energy Industry** there is an **Answer key** so that you can check your answers independently. There is also an **A–Z word list** and a **Useful phrases** list that you can refer to when preparing to speak to people in the industry. There is also a **Glossary** and a list of **Abbreviations, acronyms, and numbers** which allow you to quickly and accurately look up the most frequently used technical terms, phrases, abbreviations, and measures.

The **MultiROM** contains all the **Listening extracts** from the book. These can be played through the audio player on your computer, or through a conventional CD-player. In order to give yourself extra listening practice, listen to it in your car or download it to your MP3-player and listen when you are out and about. The **Interactive exercises** let you revise by doing exercises that cover the essential language from the book on your computer; this will be particularly valuable if you are using the book for self-study.

1 Introduction to the energy business

Work with a partner. Sort the fuels and energy sources below into the correct category. Can you add any more to the lists?

fossil fuel(s)	renewables	nuclear fuel(s)

(hard) coal   wind   oil   sun

uranium   gas   biomass   lignite

Now answer these questions.

1   What fuels and sources are used at your company, or the companies you do business with?
2   Which one is used most?
3   Where do these fuels come from?
4   Which are imported?

1 Match these different power plants to their descriptions.

1   hydro power plant
2   solar power plant
3   nuclear power plant
4   wind power plant
5   gas-fired power plant
6   run-of-river power plant
7   coal-fired power plant
8   lignite-fired power plant
9   pump-storage power plant

a   a traditional type of power plant which burns a solid, black fossil fuel
b   a power plant which pumps water back uphill into a reservoir during periods of low demand
c   a plant which uses the flow of water from a reservoir to generate electricity
d   a power station utilizing the natural flow of water in a river for generating power
e   type of power plant that uses uranium as its primary fuel
f   a power plant which uses the natural flow of air to generate electricity
g   a fossil fuel power plant which burns a solid, dark brown fuel
h   a power plant that generates electricity utilizing energy from the sun
i   a power station which burns gas as its primary fuel

AUDIO

2   **Listen to a phone call between a journalist, Colin Maitland, and the public relations officer of the company ELEC, Maria Berger. Complete the journalist's notes.**

ELEC'S fossil fuel use

_____ 1 and _____ 2

Power plants and loads

Lignite-fired plants for _____ 3 load

Gas-fired plants for _____ 4 and peak-load ranges

Gas plants also used to supply _____ 5

Technology to protect environment

ELEC say they have _____ 6 equipment installed in their plants.

Altrath plant, near Berlin

Commissioned in _____ 7 but has been _____ 8
since then.

Wind generation

Company building more power stations, but difficult to get _____
_____ 9 in some countries. ELEC views criticism that these
_____ 10 the countryside as 'exaggerated'.

What other questions would you expect the journalist to ask?

3   **Match the two parts to make phrases from the dialogue. Then listen again to check your answers.**

1	base	a	equipment
2	company	b	fuels
3	electricity	c	heating
4	energy	d	mix
5	fossil	e	policy
6	power	f	production
7	district	g	station
8	state-of-the-art	h	load

Match the expressions you have just formed to the following definitions.

9 _____ _____ = the generation of electrical power

10 _____ _____ = energy sources such as gas, oil and coal but not water and wind

11 _____ _____ = the power level at which basic demand and consumption is covered

12 _____ _____ = apparatus of the latest technological level

13 _____ _____ = the different primary fuels and sources used for energy production

14 _____ _____ = a plan of action chosen by a business or firm

15 _____ _____ = a plant in which electricity is produced

16 _____ _____ = a system of distributing heat in one centralized location, often linked to a power plant

4 **Work with a partner. The journalist Colin Maitland needs further information about ELEC's power plants, but the public relations officer is away. Use the information in the Partner Files to prepare information for his call. Use phrases from the box below.**

PARTNER FILES   Partner A   File 1, p. 56
                Partner B   File 7, p. 57

TELEPHONING FOR INFORMATION

Introductions
Hello … . This is … speaking.
Good morning. Is that …?
Hi …, it's … here.

Asking for information
I need some information about …
I'd like to have some (more) information about …
Can/Could you give me more information about …?
Can/Could you please tell me (about) …?
Who/What/When/Where/Why/How …?
What about …?

Asking for repetition
Sorry, I didn't quite catch that.
Would you mind repeating that?

Positive response
Sure.
No problem.
I'd be happy to.

Negative response
I'm afraid I can't help you there.
I'm afraid not.

DID YOU KNOW?

In English-speaking cultures, being polite is very important; this particularly applies to communication in business. For example, the phrase 'I was wondering …' can be used for requests, as in 'I was wondering if you could send the information again.' Phrases such as 'I'm afraid', 'Well actually', and 'Unfortunately' are used to introduce something negative or make complaints. Look at these examples:
May I smoke?
Well actually, it is forbidden in this building.
I'm afraid the last bill was not accurate.
Not using such phrases can be seen as being too direct.

5   **Read what people say about different fuels and energy sources. Which bubble is mainly about the following?**

☐ 1   public perception of energy and the energy industry
☐ 2   the effects on the environment of different sources of energy
☐ 3   the availability of renewable sources
☐ 4   the reliability and efficiency of fossil fuels

a
Coal and lignite are the most reliable fuels. We'll depend on them more as gas and oil disappear. There may be a few problems with emissions, but these can easily be solved. They're also very versatile and can be used to produce electricity and heat our homes efficiently.

b
Fossil fuels are harmful; think how they affect our atmosphere and countryside. We can't build our future energy planning on them. We have to think differently. The sun is a clean energy source, and the potential for providing us with power is enormous! What's more we can install solar cells on buildings, which will reduce the requirement for large power stations.

c
Solar power is good as far as it goes, but what do you do when the sun isn't shining? In some countries there are often cloudy skies, and in some countries there are only four hours of sunlight per day in winter. Wind on the other hand is always at our disposal – more than the sun anyway. We can use this source to cover our needs.

d
The most important thing is to educate people about energy. It may be true that fossil fuels and other sources have some drawbacks, but there are many positive aspects. We should focus on informing people; how they see energy is important.

Say which of the above statements you agree with. Use phrases from below.

EXPRESSING OPINIONS AND AGREEMENT OR DISAGREEMENT		
Giving your opinion	**Agreeing**	**Asking for opinions**
I think/feel (that) …	Quite right.	What do you think?
In my opinion …	That's true.	How do you see it?
In my view …	I quite agree.	
Clarifying	**Disagreeing**	
So you're saying …	Yes, but …	
You mean …	Actually, I think …	
What do you mean exactly by …?	To be honest …	
	I don't quite agree.	

6   **Work with a partner. How do you rate these different types of power plant on a scale from 1 (good) to 6 (very poor/bad)? Use the phrases on page 8.**

Power Plant Type	Rating				
	Public perception	Effects on environment	Availability of primary fuel/source	Reliability	Efficiency
Hydro power plant					
Solar power plant					
Nuclear power plant					
Wind power plant					
Gas-fired power plant					
Lignite-fired power plant					
Biomass-fired power plant					

Compare your results with other students and give reasons for your rating.

7   **ELEC is creating some basic educational publicity material. Complete these statements with expressions from the box, and then number the statements in the correct order.**

connection • distribution network • facility • municipal utility •
overhead lines • supplier • transmission network •

☐   a   And that is how the power eventually reaches you, via the
_____ that links your home to the network.

1   b   From the power station, high-voltage electricity enters what
we call the _____.

☐   c   The utility transmits, distributes and delivers electricity (and possibly
gas) from a _____ which it owns and operates to the final
customer. Delivery is via what we call the _____.

☐   d   This supplier is the company from whom you, the customer, get your
energy. It is often a _____, owned by a city or town.

☐   e   This is a system of transmission towers and _____,
through which the electricity makes its way to the _____.

8 Complete this text from ELEC's website with the correct form of the verb.

The Players
of the Power Business

| About ELEC → | Energy supply → | How it works → | | Keyword search 🔍 |

From generator to supplier to customer

Electricity _is generated_ [1] (generate) by power stations and _____ [2] (feed) into the high-voltage transmission network. Via transmission towers and overhead lines it _____ [3] (transport) to the local supplier, an organization which _____ [4] (own) by the municipality or the regional subsidiary of a larger power company. This local supplier is normally the first point of contact for the customer. Connections _____ [5] (organize) by this company, and power _____ [6] (deliver) to the customer.

Customer choice and the role of the regulator

In some countries the supplier can _____ [7] (choose) by the customer as some markets _____ [8] (liberalize). In order to ensure that there is fair competition, some states have set up regulators. Their main task is to ensure that there is non-discriminatory third-party access. The grid fees that the operators charge for using the networks _____ [9] (also control). When prices _____ [10] (increase) by the supplier, this _____ [11] (also monitor) by the regulator.

ℹ Site map   ℹ Legal   ℹ Access   ℹ Disclaimer

DID YOU KNOW?

The first practical generator was built by Thomas Edison, the famous inventor. He used it to provide electricity for his laboratory and then later to generate power for the first New York street to be illuminated by electric lamps. Unlike most AC (alternating current) generators of today, Edison's apparatus produced DC (direct current).

9 **Find a word or expression in the text in exercise 8 which means the same as the following.**

1 pylon
2 a company owned by a parent company
3 country
4 to watch and check continuously

5 to make certain
6 grid
7 to demand an amount of money for goods or services

10 **Complete this table and then the text below with the correct word or expression.**

	Noun	Verb	Company/Person
1	generation		generator
2	transmission		
3	sales		
4		to distribute	
5		to regulate	
6		to liberalize	– – –
7	supply		

Is the regulator the answer?

In European countries where the energy market has been liberalized, many energy customers are not pleased with the results of this _____[8] process. They claim there are no real benefits. They see energy companies making large profits, firstly through the _____[9] of power and then as grid operators when they charge outside companies high grid fees for the _____[10] of electricity through their networks. Many see _____[11] as the answer as this should force companies to consider their prices. This will probably make it less profitable to _____[12] the final customer with electricity and gas. Each company's overall _____[13] volume is set to decrease as more firms enter the market.

DID YOU KNOW?

In some countries, the company which operates a high-voltage grid is called the TSO (Transmission Systems Operator). The company which runs a distribution network is sometimes called the DSO (Distribution Systems Operator).

AUDIO

3

11   **At a follow-up meeting to the phone call in exercise 2, Maria explains ELEC's structure to Colin. Listen to her explanation and complete this chart taken from ELEC's annual report. Then say which division the statements under the chart refer to.**

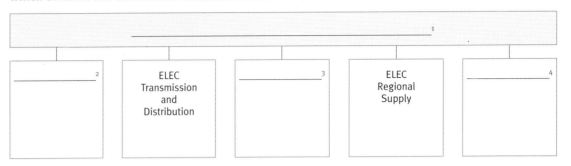

5   It has networks in many European countries.
6   It is a buying operation, procuring energy for the European supply company.
7   It procures gas from partners in Russia.
8   It is a company in its own right.
9   It runs opencast mines producing lignite and coal.
10   This division has a lot of subsidiaries each responsible for a specific geographical area.
11   This division is in the process of being consolidated under one management structure.

Now outline the structure of the company you work for or do business with.
How does it compare to ELEC´s structure?

12   **Complete this puzzle with words from the unit, and find the person who buys electricity or gas in column a.**

1   a fossil fuel used for generating electricity
2   a company which transports electricity to homes and businesses
3   the first of the three load levels; the other two are *intermediate* and *peak*
4   a company which runs a network system
5   a company that generates, transmits, distributes and supplies electricity or gas from facilities which it owns and operates (2 words – 4, 8)
6   the process whereby a company transports electricity at high-voltage levels
7   a company which produces electricity
8   what a company is involved in when it buys and sells electricity or gas at the energy exchanges

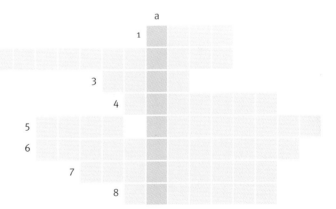

TPUT   **Which countries does your country import its gas from? Read this newspaper article and discuss the questions.**

Issues

Gas in Crisis?

The world is changing fast. There is an energy crisis on the horizon for Europe. If we take natural gas as an example it would seem at first glance that countries such as Norway, Britain and the

Netherlands have sufficient gas reserves to supply Europe for some time to come. However, this is misleading; most of these reserves will be used up over the next ten to twenty years. Even if more deposits are found in the North Sea or the Atlantic Ocean the problem will still not be solved. The continent must turn to Russia where there are

huge quantities of gas underground. This country is in the happy position of being the gas giant of the world.

Other nations are also approaching Moscow to cover their energy requirements. The economies of countries such as China and India are expanding dramatically and they are going to need massive amounts of energy, which includes gas. Will there be enough of this commodity to satisfy the needs of Asia and Europe? This is by no means certain, and the consequence could be a shortage of gas imports, which could lead to power cuts in some European countries in the future.

There is one other source of gas – LNG, liquefied natural gas. This is transported by ship from such places as the Arabian Peninsula. Nevertheless, it is questionable if these supplies can ever be a realistic alternative to gas which is imported by pipeline; the simple fact is that the volumes shipped would never meet demand.

People are therefore right to be worried. Political leaders and companies must tackle this issue; we need a secure and reliable supply of gas for the long term. This inevitably means that wholesale prices will soar, but this is still better than the nightmare scenario of freezing in our homes or having no power for our industry.

OVER TO YOU

- Is there really a gas crisis? What do you think?
- What about oil and coal? Do you think there will be enough reserves for the future?
- How do you think China will develop its economy and how will it power its industry?
- How can your country ensure gas supplies?

2 Markets and customers

Discuss the questions with a partner.

- Can you switch your gas or electricity supplier in your country?
- How easy is it to do? What would encourage you to do it, or prevent you from doing it?

Now decide how important the following factors would be if you wanted to switch your electricity and/or gas supplier.

The new supplier should:	Very important	Not so important
1 offer a cheaper price than the current supplier.		
2 guarantee security of supply.		
3 supply both electricity and gas.		
4 take care of all formalities regarding the changeover from the old to the new contract.		
5 send clear and accurate bills.		
6 offer the customer different ways of paying bills (direct debit, credit card, etc).		
7 provide online services (e.g. for meter readings).		
8 give advice on energy efficiency.		
9 have a 24-hour helpline (call centre).		
10 have offices in the same town as my home.		

1 **Work with a partner. How are these types of customer defined in the company you work for? Give examples for each one.**

1   a residential/retail customer
2   a business customer
3   an industrial customer

Discuss the following questions about industrial customers.

1   What are the largest five industries in your country or region? Use those listed below to help you. What are their products? Who are their clients?

> **Industries**
>
> aluminium industry • chemical industry • steel industry • pharmaceutical industry • pulp and paper industry • plastic industry • textile industry • automotive industry •

2   How are they supplied with power? Do some of them have their own power plants or are they supplied by other energy companies?
3   Which consume(s) the most energy? Rank them on a scale of 1–5 according to how much electricity they consume.
4   What do large industrial companies want from energy companies?

2 **Paul Robben from AECP – the Association of European Chemical Producers – is talking to Anna Smith from the energy company ELEC. You are sitting in on the meeting. Listen and say whether the following statements are true or false.**

1   AECP has established an energy procurement unit.
2   Its aim is to harmonize the terms under which it does business with its various suppliers.
3   AECP wants there to be one key account manager at ELEC.
4   A key issue for AECP is security of supply.
5   AECP expects its requirements to remain constant.

Listen again and complete notes for the minutes of the meeting under the following headings.

1 Members of AECP	
2 Development of wholesale prices	
3 AECP's objectives	
4 Forecasts on AECP's future energy consumption	
5 Next step	

3 These graphs show developments mentioned in exercise 2. What does each graph show? If you are not sure, listen to the dialogue again.

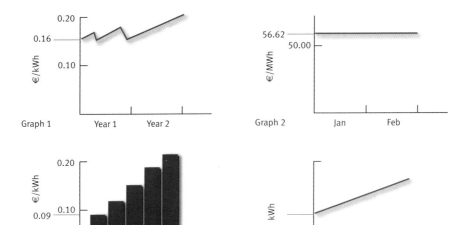

4 Match the statements that have the same meaning. Then decide which graph each pair refers to.

1   It's going to grow.
2   It has remained stable.
3   They've doubled.
4   It has fluctuated.

a   It's held steady.
b   It's been volatile.
c   We expect it to rise.
d   There's been a 100% increase.

5 Match the expression with each graph below. Add any expressions that you know.

decline • fall sharply • ~~fluctuate~~ • hit a low and then recover • remain stable •
level off • fall back and then pick up again • peak and then fall back • increase steeply •
rise steadily •

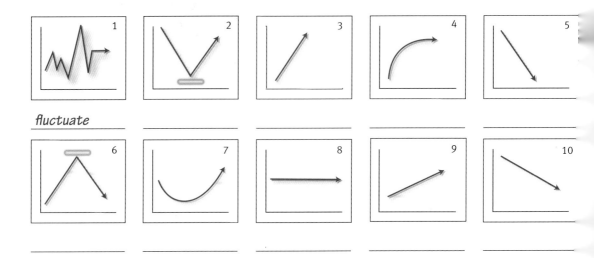

fluctuate

6 This graph shows the development of the EEX electricity spot price in 2009. Continue the following description. Use expressions from exercises 4 and 5.

The graph shows the development of the EEX electricity spot price in 2009. The price started at ...

Choose a graph describing a trend from your own company on a subject that you are familiar with. Present it to the other students. Use phrases from the box.

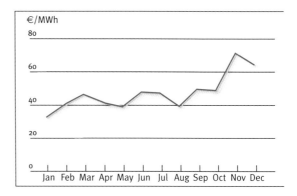

DESCRIBING TRENDS, DEVELOPMENTS AND CONSEQUENCES

The graph shows ...	This led to ...
You can see here that ...	This resulted in ...
This happened/occurred because ...	This was due to ...
We expected this change, but ...	This happened as a result of ...
Although there was a fall/rise ...	This happened because of ...

7 Write sentences describing developments and consequences, using phrases from the right-hand column of the box.

1 a surge in the gas price/harsh winter

_____

2 the economy picked up/increase in high-street spending

_____

3 a reduction in turnover/cost-cutting programme

_____

4 a power cut/collapse of the grid

_____

5 consumers can choose their supplier/liberalization

_____

6 the volatile political situation/uncertainty in the market

_____

7 more wind farms have been built/financial support from the state

_____

_____

Now describe some developments and their consequences from your own company.

AUDIO

5

8   **AECP and ELEC (see exercise 2) signed a contract about energy supply. But then Anna Smith received a phone call. Listen and decide which four statements describe the situation.**

1   The weather has resulted in a crisis situation in the Netherlands.
2   The distribution network has gone down, but the transmission grid is unaffected.
3   The Dutch-German interconnector is out of action.
4   The problem has fortunately now been rectified.
5   Power is being fed in from France and Belgium.
6   There will be questions about liability and insurance.
7   AECP members may look for another supplier.

Complete this internal memo by Anna in a suitable way.

AECP crisis in Netherlands

Bad weather has disrupted supply to _____ .

They are _____, and operating on _____

generators at present. _____ are working to resolve the

situation, but AECP has brought up the issue of _____ and

is talking about _____ – even though it's clearly a

question of _____ .

DID YOU KNOW?

UCTE stands for the Union for the Co-ordination of Transmission of Electricity. The members of this association are the transmission systems operators in continental Europe stretching from Spain through to Poland and Greece. It ensures the synchronous operation of interconnected power systems. A similar organization, Nordel, exists in the countries of Scandinavia.

---

9   **Match the expressions to the definitions.**

1   circuit breaker

2   force majeure

3   power outage

4   power surge

5   substation

a   a unit which increases or decreases voltage levels
b   a sharp, temporary rise in current or voltage levels which can cause damage to electrical equipment
c   equipment which protects electrical apparatus from a sharp rise in current levels by switching off electrical current automatically
d   loss of electrical power to an area
e   an unexpected or uncontrollable event; nobody is at fault or responsible for subsequent damage

10   **Complete this letter of complaint from Paul Robben to Anna Smith with the expressions from the box.**

> Before writing this letter • Dear Anna • He assured me • I look forward to hearing from you • I therefore suggest • May I remind you • I might add • We are extremely concerned • Yours sincerely •

Association of European Chemical Producers
Energy Procurement Unit

Oranjeweg 118 • 3014 LA Rotterdam • Netherlands

Ms Anna Smith
ELEC International
Business Sales Unit
Hohewall 34
D-10423 Berlin
Germany

10 April 20..

_____ [1]

I was somewhat dismayed to find out that just three weeks after I had signed the purchase contract with ELEC for our organization there was a sudden and complete breakdown in electricity supply to two of our members' production facilities in the Netherlands. _____ [2] that under the terms of our agreement ELEC is obliged to guarantee security of supply.

_____ [3] I spoke to one of ELEC's engineers. He went into great technical detail about power surges and outages in the surrounding areas. _____ [4] that it was only due to our own circuit breakers that our plants were not severely damaged.

_____ [5] that his team was working around the clock to remedy the situation. He implied it was force majeure; this remains to be verified.

_____ [6] about the situation and are questioning whether ELEC can supply power to all our production locations throughout Europe.

_____ [7] we meet to discuss this most unfortunate state of affairs. I propose this meeting should take place at our headquarters in Rotterdam next week on Tuesday, April 17th at 10.00 a.m.

_____ [8].

_____ [9],

Dr. Paul Robben
Managing Director
AECP Energy Procurement Unit

11 Write a reply to the letter on page 19 using phrases from the box.

REPLYING TO LETTERS OF COMPLAINT	
I fully understand your concern but ...	We are taking this matter very seriously.
I would like to stress that ...	I would also like to assure you that ...
These are circumstances beyond our control.	We are making every effort to ...
Nevertheless, ...	We are doing our utmost to ...

If the crisis in the Netherlands happened to your company, how would it be resolved?

12 Work with a partner. Use the information in the Partner Files to do this role-play.

Paul phones Anna to talk about the agenda of their meeting. Prepare your roles and then role-play the telephone call. Use phrases for agreeing and disagreeing from page 8, and from the box below.

PARTNER FILES
Partner A   File 2, p. 56
Partner B   File 8, p. 57

DEALING WITH A COMPLAINT		
Giving assurance	**Sticking to a position**	**Strong disagreement**
I can assure you (that) ...	I really must insist (that) ...	I can't accept that.
You have my assurance (that) ...	Our position remains the same.	That's not on.
We're doing all we can to ...	Look, ...	That's quite impossible.

13 Discuss with a partner which statement describes the market your company operates in.

1
In our country we have a very regulated market. We and our competitors have to comply with a lot of rules and regulations when doing business and it's quite difficult to do things independently.

2
Our market is very liberalized. It's totally open to all players; companies offer gas and electricity at competitive prices to consumers and there is little state intervention.

Is there a lot of competition in your market? How difficult is it for new entrants to enter the market? What barriers do they face?

TPUT

How do power companies view organizations which look after consumers' interests?
Read this Internet text about Energywatch in the UK and discuss the questions.

Energywatch merged into Consumer Focus

Energywatch, the former independent watchdog for gas and electricity consumers, has been merged into a new organization called Consumer Focus that looks after consumer interests.

Consumer focus is for energy consumers what Greenpeace is for the environment – a campaign group that champions a better deal for people and promotes innovation for consumer benefit. It takes up complaints on behalf of consumers and has greater powers than its predecessors. It acts on behalf of vulnerable consumers who may feel exploited by powerful energy companies.

Consumer Focus employs 170 people and has a budget of £15 million. It is able to investigate consumer complaints that it feels will be of benefit to the public at large. It can also demand information from utility companies.

One of its priorities is to tackle the issue of fuel poverty in Britain. Fuel poverty is defined as a household that spends more than ten percent of its income on fuel. Utility companies are usually quick to pass on rises in fuel costs to their customers and Consumer Focus estimates that five million British households faced fuel poverty in the winter of 2008. Ed Mayo, the chief executive of Consumer Focus, says, "Customers across the country will be seriously worried about bills escalating through winter while the regulator (Ofgem) consults with industry. We urge energy companies to take action now by boosting their social tariffs."

Although there are advantages to having one organization look after all consumer complaints, some people are worried that energy will not always be the priority of such a big organization. "Will Consumer Focus really be able to do anything about what foreign companies charge for fuel?" asked one worried consumer. "Wouldn't Energywatch have been better at dealing with this kind of specific problem?"

Ed Mayo does not agree. "As one organization, we take a more co-ordinated approach to tackling the issues that affect us all. We are able to engage more effectively with government, business and regulators and we have stronger powers and more teeth."

OVER TO YOU

- Do you think such a watchdog agency is necessary? Give your reasons.
- How do such organizations influence the overall strategy and policy of energy companies?
- Are energy companies forced by legislation to cap prices in your country? If so, outline how this is done.
- Does the energy industry in your country have an organization which looks after the interests of power companies? If so, how does it do this?

3 Protecting the environment

STARTER **Do you agree or disagree with these ideas or are you not sure? Discuss your answers with a partner.**

	Agree	Disagree	Not sure
1 It is not necessary to educate people on the issue of protecting the environment.	O	O	O
2 Cooking with gas is more environmentally friendly than cooking with electricity.	O	O	O
3 Consumers should be obliged to buy only energy-saving electrical equipment.	O	O	O
4 Fossil fuel power plants should be totally replaced by ones using renewable sources.	O	O	O
5 A speed limit of 90 km/h should be established throughout the European Union to conserve oil stocks.	O	O	O
6 People should be encouraged to use public transport and not use their car.	O	O	O
7 All houses and buildings should be checked each year for their energy efficiency.	O	O	O
8 A massive green tax should be put on long-distance air travel to protect the environment.	O	O	O

A leaflet entitled *Energy Saving Tips in the Home* is being developed. Write down your suggestions for tips and compare them with the rest of the class. As a group decide on the best ones.

1   **Anna Smith at ELEC received this email invitation to a seminar. Complete the email with the expressions from the box.**

> by invitation only • Could you please let me know • I would also be grateful •
> It is with great pleasure • It would be beneficial • Kind regards •
> please see attachment • to get to know •

Dear Ms Smith,

_____[1] that we invite you to take part in the tenth International Forum for Energy to discuss the image of the energy industry. This three-day event will be taking place at the International Hotel in Dubai from May 5th–8th of this year (_____ _____[2] for more details).

Participation in this forum is _____[3], and the main topic will be public relations regarding the image of the energy industry as a whole, and how this image affects our business. Jane Hall, the CEO of ELEC, will be giving a talk on how ELEC is approaching the subject of public relations and the lessons we can learn from this experience. There will also be an opportunity _____[4] other delegates.

_____[5] if you wish to attend this seminar by sending me an email?

_____[6] if you could inform me about any other issues you may wish to raise during these three days. There will be an open forum on Thursday evening, May 6th, in which delegates can discuss topics which they feel are important for the industry.

_____[7], however, if delegates informed me about what they wish to discuss beforehand so that we can draw up a relevant agenda for the evening.

I look forward to hearing from you.

_____[8],

Abdullah Al-Naimi

You are Anna. Write an answer to Abdullah Al-Naimi accepting the invitation. Ask him also to send the attachment again as it did not come through to you. Tell him that in the open forum you would like to raise the issue of biofuels. Use phrases from the box to help you.

REPLYING TO INVITATIONS

Accepting invitations	**Making requests**
I was delighted to receive your kind invitation …	Would/Could you please …?
Thank you very much for your kind invitation to take part in …	I would be grateful if you could …
I would very much like to attend.	I would appreciate it if you could …

2   **Read this extract from a brochure created for the forum. Decide whether the statements that follow are true or false. Correct the false statements.**

International Forum for Energy

Dear Delegates,

I am delighted to have the opportunity to speak to you all at the tenth International Forum for Energy. The main focus of my talk will be on how we are all ambassadors, not only for our companies or organizations but also for our industry as a whole. We all need to be aware of the challenges that face us – particularly our image concerning the issue of the environment – and we all have to be more proactive regarding this matter.

ELEC statistics are representative of the industry as a whole and speak for themselves. 40% of our generating capacity is accounted for by lignite and coal, 25% by gas, 20% is attributable to nuclear energy, and just 15% accounted for by hydro and renewables. The industry is therefore seen by the public as one of the main culprits regarding climate change, air pollution, rising sea levels, and other environmental problems including the hole in the ozone layer.

This is despite the fact that we have invested a lot of effort and money in finding solutions. All fossil fuel plants have been fitted with desulphurization plants to reduce emissions of greenhouse gases such as sulphur dioxide – one of the main causes of acid rain. We have also developed combustion technology to decrease carbon dioxide emissions, and we have installed denox equipment to reduce nitrogen oxides. We are also heavily involved in emissions trading.

There are many, particularly in the media and in politics, who would wish to highlight the negative aspects without even mentioning the measures that we have implemented over the last few years. This forum will give us all the opportunity to discuss the issues and challenges so that we are able to respond in a professional and appropriate manner.

I am sure that we will have some very interesting and thought-provoking discussions.

Jane Hall
Chief Executive officer

1   People see the energy industry as 'clean'.
2   Gas is the least important source in the ELEC's energy mix.
3   Nuclear energy makes up 15% of generating capacity.
4   ELEC has invested a lot of money in technology to reduce emissions.
5   It is well known that a lot of measures to reduce emissions have been implemented.
6   Managers have to be able to answer questions concerning their companies' environmental record.

3 **Read Jane Hall's message again. Find expressions that fit into these sentences.**

1 The heating up of the atmosphere is caused by _____ _____ .

2 The main cause of damage to trees is _____ _____ . It has been estimated that more than 60% of forests are affected.

3 The _____ in the _____ over the South Pole and Australia has raised levels of ultraviolet radiation. This can cause severe sunburn.

4 _____ _____ is one of the emissions from a power plant burning fossil fuels.

5 Winters are becoming milder and wetter, and average temperatures year-round are increasing. These are two major signs of _____ _____ .

6 Generators that pollute too much can buy credits or allowances from other companies in a system of _____ _____ .

7 The emitting of harmful gases into the atmosphere is called _____ _____ .

8 The Netherlands is in danger of being flooded due to a rise in _____ _____ .

9 A _____ _____ is the equipment in a power plant which removes sulphur dioxide.

4 **Listen to a presentation given by Jane Hall at the forum. In which order does she do the following?**

- [ ] a describe ELEC's present performance
- [ ] b invite questions
- [ ] c mention future plans for new plants
- [ ] d raise the issue of lobbying
- [ ] e welcome delegates

Now complete this summary by one of the delegates.

CEO Jane Hall's key point was the need to
_____ at both a national
and _____ level on
the issues of _____
_____, so that
all companies can _____ on
the same basis.

5 **Which of these phrases did Jane Hall use in her presentation? Listen again and check.**

GIVING A PRESENTATION

Opening
Let me first introduce myself.
I'm/My name is … .
In this talk I want/would like to …
I'll begin by (+ -ing form of verb).
I'm going to be covering …
Let's start with (+ noun).

Introducing other factors or points
If I could now turn to …
Now, turning to …
Let me move on to …

Introducing graphs and diagrams
I'd like you to look at this graph/diagram/(pie)
   chart/transparency/slide.

Comparing factors
First of all …
Firstly …, secondly …, thirdly …
On the one hand …, on the other hand …

Concluding
That completes my overview (of …).
So, to summarize/sum up …

Questions
Please don't hesitate to interrupt me if you have
   any questions.
If you have any questions, I'll be pleased to answer
   them at the end.

Finishing
Thank you for your attention.

Now prepare and give a short presentation on your job and the department in which you work. Use phrases from above.

UDIO
7

6 Another speaker at the forum gives a talk on emissions trading and some research projects. Listen to what he says and make notes.

Emissions trading

_____
_____
_____
_____

Imagine you are representing your company at an international conference. Explain in your own words how emissions trading works.

7 At the conference you are asked the following questions. How would you answer?

1
How do you see the overall image of the energy industry in your country as regards environment protection?

2
How does the government in your country support protecting the environment? Are there any financial incentives?

3
What precisely does your company do to protect the environment? Do you have any schemes like carbon capture or designing CO2 neutral plants?

4
How great is the impact of emission control costs on the price of electricity?

5
Does the cost of protecting the environment have any repercussions on the competitiveness of your country's economy in world markets?

6
What programmes, if any, does the company you work for have to help customers save energy?

DID YOU KNOW?

As part of the UK's overall energy policy, the Scottish Executive (government) has set a new target – 40% of all electricity generated in Scotland should come from renewable sources by 2020. This is not as far-fetched as it sounds as much of the land in Scotland is exposed to winds which are favourable for wind generation. The other option is to harness water or tidal energy – Scotland is a world leader in tidal research.

8 Work in groups of three. Use the information in the Partner Files to do this role-play.

At the seminar in Dubai, ELEC managers were asked to brainstorm ideas on how to improve the company's environmental image. Prepare your roles and then role-play the situation. Agree on a set of the best five proposals.

PARTNER FILES ▷ Partner A File 3, p.56
Partner B File 9, p.57
Partner C File 13, p.58

9 What do you think these newspaper articles are about? Write the first paragraph of each article. Then compare and discuss them with other members of the class.

1
Europe to Cut Greenhouse Emissions by 20 %

2
Wind Power Not Reliable

3
Environment Protection Costs Jobs

4
The First Step to Improve Your Carbon Footprint

5
Global Warming –
All the Fault of Energy Companies

6
Green Tax for Air Travel and Generators

7
Coal Industry to Pay for CO_2 Emissions

10 There are a lot of acronyms and abbreviations used in the energy industry. What do the following stand for, and in which context are they used (e.g. generation, emissions, etc.)?

1 CO2   4 V   7 DSO
2 SO2   5 UCTE   8 MW
3 CHP   6 TSO   9 kWh

11 Complete this puzzle with words from the unit and find an essential function for most companies in column a.

1 What you do when you take and store a substance for a long period. You do it with carbon dioxide, for example, and pump it into the ground.
2 The type of gases which warm the earth's atmosphere.
3 Financial support from the state, usually for industrial purposes.
4 Energy sources such as wind, the sun, etc.
5 A diagram with a horizontal and vertical axis.
6 The first element in CO2.
7 The type of rain produced by some emissions from power stations and which badly affects trees.
8 To alter something or to make something different.

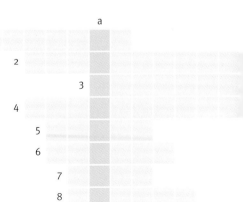

TPUT

Which organization makes sure that emission limits are observed in your country?
Read this newspaper article about the Kyoto Protocol and discuss the questions.

The Kyoto Protocol

The Kyoto Protocol is the name of an international treaty to reduce the amount of greenhouse gas emissions which came into effect in 2005. The signatories of this binding agreement are divided into two categories, so-called "Annex 1" and "Non-Annex 1" countries. The former comprises developed countries which made a commitment to

cut greenhouse gas emissions to 5% below 1990 levels by 2008–2012. Under the terms of the agreement, the latter had no actual mandatory greenhouse emission restrictions but were to be able to sell carbon credits on the international market to Annex 1 buyers as part of any emission reduction project implemented in these countries. This was to be on a voluntary basis.

A number of countries did not ratify the treaty, notably the U.S.A – the largest emitter of greenhouse gases – and (initially) Australia. In addition, India and China, which have large populations and rapidly expanding economies, did not set emission limits, at least not under the terms of the Protocol. This was justified by the fact that these countries were not the main contributors of emissions during the process of the world's industrialization period i.e. the 19th and 20th centuries.

This brought the whole project into doubt in terms of reaching the targets envisaged. Indeed, some critics called the Kyoto Protocol flawed because in their view it favoured some countries at the expense of others. Others said that the treaty should only be seen as a first step to manage greenhouse emissions on a global scale, and that stricter measures and limits should be implemented as soon as possible, which should be adopted by all countries not just the developed ones.

Since the Protocol came into force, the majority of politicians, economists and environmentalists have reached the view that if nothing is done to address climate change we will be heading for economic, social and environmental collapse throughout the world. This has led to further conferences aimed at drawing up a more binding treaty than the Kyoto Protocol.

OVER TO YOU

- What do you think of the Kyoto Protocol? Did it set attainable goals?
- Are industrialized countries to blame for climate change? What about the position of energy companies?
- What about the position of China and India? Is it fair? Why, or why not?

4 The nuclear issue

What words do you associate with nuclear energy? Complete the diagram below, then compare and discuss your diagram with other members of your class.

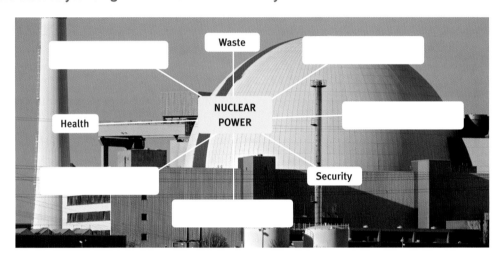

Waste

NUCLEAR POWER

Health

Security

1 How much do you know about nuclear energy? Work with a partner and complete this quiz.

1 Which country produces the most uranium for the world market?

a Russia   b USA   c Canada

2 Which country generates 75% of its electricity on the basis of nuclear power?

a France   b UK   c Germany

3 In which year did the accident occur in the Three Mile Island nuclear power plant?

a 1979   b 1986   c 1992

4 How many nuclear reactors are operated in Japan for the purpose of generating electricity?

a 35   b 45   c 55

5 In which country are there no nuclear power stations in operation?

a Finland
b Austria
c Czech Republic

6 When and in which country was the world's first full-scale commercial nuclear plant commissioned?

a 1951 in the USA
b 1956 in the UK
c 1962 in the former USSR

Now discuss these questions briefly in your group.

1   Is the image of nuclear power in your country generally positive or negative? Give some details.
2   Are new plants being built? If so, outline where this is being done.
3   Is nuclear power being phased out? If so, outline the reasons.
4   Are nuclear plants economically viable when compared with other types of power stations? State what you think.
5   What is the situation in your country concerning the storage and disposal of nuclear waste?

DID YOU KNOW?

The very first time that electricity was generated using a nuclear reactor was in 1951 at an experimental power plant near Arco, Idaho in the USA.

---

2   **Uranium is the basis of nuclear energy. Work with a partner and put these sentences in the right order so that they describe the processes the uranium goes through.**

☐   a   After that, the uranium ore is crushed into a fine powder.
☐   b   First of all, uranium is extracted from opencast or underground mining.
☐   c   The next step is fuel fabrication. The nuclear fuel is transformed into pellets.
☐   d   This yellow cake is then enriched to increase the proportion of uranium 235, which is essential in the nuclear fission process.
☐   e   Finally, the spent fuel must be reprocessed and stored long term underground.
☐   f   Following that, they are formed into rods and placed in the reactor pressure vessel.
☐   g   In the reactor pressure vessel, heat is produced through a fissile reaction and eventually the uranium is used up.
☐   h   After crushing, the powder is then purified; the substance at the end of this process is called 'yellow cake'.

AUDIO

8

3   ELEC's nuclear power division is considering entering into a joint venture with JEPCO, a Japanese power company. A guide is giving a group of visitors from JEPCO a tour of one of ELEC's nuclear power plants. Listen to this talk on its operation and label the diagram.

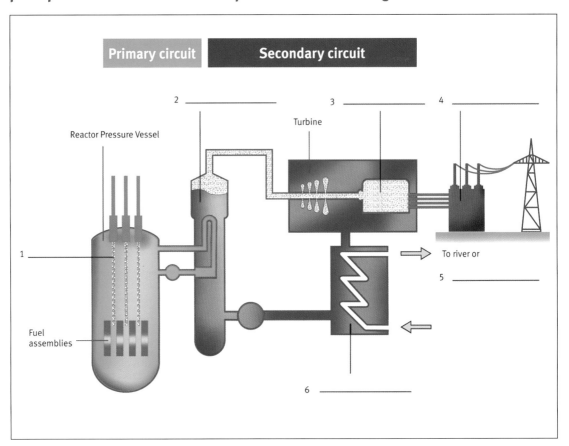

Listen again and take notes on the purpose and functions of these parts of the power station. You will need the notes for exercise 4.

1   The reactor pressure vessel
2   The primary circuit
3   The steam generator
4   The transformers
5   The condenser

4   Put yourself in the position of the guide in exercise 3. Use the diagram, your notes, and phrases from below to describe the whole process in your own words.

DESCRIBING A PROCESS	
Firstly/First of all ...	Following that ...
After that ...	Finally ...
The next step/stage is ...	The final step ...
Then ...	

5　Read these sentences from a publicity brochure describing the process of waste disposal. Put the sentences in the right order and link them with phrases from above.

☐ a _____ the spent fuel rods are extracted from the reactor.

☐ b _____ the waste needs to be buried deep underground in a safe location.

☐ c Eventually the spent fuel has to be reprocessed, so _____ that it is transported to a reprocessing plant, such as Sellafield in the UK and La Hague in France. There it is vitrified and sealed in steel canisters.

☐ d _____ the waste is transferred to a site where interim storage is possible. There are a number of such sites in Europe.

```
┌──────────┐     ┌──────────┐     ┌──────────┐     ┌──────────┐
│ Reactor  │ --> │ Interim  │ --> │Reprocessing│ --> │  Final   │
│          │     │ storage  │     │  plant    │     │ storage  │
└──────────┘     └──────────┘     └──────────┘     └──────────┘
```

6　A working group at ELEC is visiting JEPCO to find out about their arrangements for waste disposal, in order to formulate a new public relations strategy. Listen and note the key issues.

Storage and reprocessing

_____

_____

_____

Long-term disposal

_____

_____

_____

_____

7   **Match the two parts to make expressions from the discussion in exercise 6. Listen again if necessary.**

1   public
2   government
3   disposal
4   spent
5   safety
6   reprocessing
7   interim
8   waste

a   measures
b   storage
c   plants
d   fuel
e   facility
f   resistance
g   disposal
h   legislation

Now complete these sentences using the correct expression.

9   Companies which operate nuclear power plants must have a programme for _____

_____ so that unwanted products can be dealt with safely.

10   There are facilities for _____ at nuclear power stations to store waste for a limited time until a permanent location can be found.

11   _____ is the uranium which has been used up.

12   The two most well-known _____ in Europe are Sellafield in the UK and La Hague in France.

13   Waste can be stored in a _____.

14   There is a lot of _____ to nuclear power; some people just don't like it.

15   Other members of the public are not convinced of the _____

_____ at nuclear power stations, and think radiation will leak into the atmosphere.

16   Many people have no trust in the politicians who draft new _____

_____ regarding nuclear power.

8 **ELEC and JEPCO have approached a firm of PR consultants, Finley Consultants, to advise them on a coherent PR strategy for their joint venture. Read this excerpt from the consultants' report.**

This is a time of great opportunities for the nuclear energy industry. With the price of fossil fuels reaching an all-time high, the debate about peak oil, and the environmental concerns around fossil fuels, nuclear has a real chance of becoming the leading global power source. This really could be the end for fossil fuels. However, the nuclear industry, for historical reasons, has been viewed with suspicion by the general public. The Chernobyl disaster, as well as more minor incidents such as the recent uranium spillage in Bollene, France, contribute to the fact that people are still to be convinced that nuclear is the clean, safe power of the future.

The value of the JEPCO/ELEC alliance is based on being able to demonstrate that the combined experience of both companies, in Japan and Europe, will translate into secure nuclear power stations and safe, long-term waste management. The PR strategy should focus on the advances made to the construction of nuclear power, provisions for reprocessing waste in Japan, and the impact of new research on waste storage. This positive PR message, by showing voters that nuclear power is an energy that can be trusted, will help governments put forward the argument for the construction of new nuclear power stations.

JEPCOs Hiro Takayashi has requested a response from ELEC's Jane Hall to Finley Consultants' report from managers. Write him an email and include the following points.

1 Agree that nuclear power has a real opportunity to grow.
2 Disagree about this being the end for fossil fuels. There is plenty of coal. Political factors affect the price of oil, not just availability.
3 Stress that the PR strategy should highlight that the next generation of nuclear power stations will be built to resist terrorist attacks and powerful earthquakes.
4 Point out that it is important to admit that, so far, there is no totally safe way of storing nuclear waste for thousands of years, so that it remains a danger.
5 Suggest a meeting with lobbyists to discuss the next steps for the PR strategy.

9 **Mary Brown, Jane Hall's secretary, phones Jacques Royale of the strategy unit to set up a time for a meeting to discuss the proposals. Put the dialogue into the right order.**

☐	a *Jacques*	Hello. Jacques Royale speaking.
☐	b *Mary*	OK, how about Tuesday, March 6th at three p.m?
☐	c *Jacques*	I could make four. Could you change it to four p.m?
☐	d *Mary*	Hello, Jacques. Mary Brown here.
☐	e *Jacques*	Let me check my diary. I'm afraid that's not so good as I've got a meeting with some members of the supervisory board most of Monday morning.
☐	f *Mary*	Yes, that's fine, four is also OK. I'll send everybody a quick email to confirm everything.
☐	g *Jacques*	Hi Mary. What can I do for you?
☐	h *Mary*	Yes. Bye, Jacques.
☐	i *Jacques*	Great. Well, I'll probably see you next week.
☐	j *Mary*	I'm phoning to set up a meeting between Jane and Mr Takayashi and the strategy unit to discuss the proposals made by Finley Consultants. Would next Monday at nine a.m. suit you?

10   The strategy unit has prepared a list of arguments for maintaining nuclear power.
Work with a partner and rate them on a scale of 1–3 (1 = very important, 2 = important,
3 = not important). Then discuss results in the class.

Nuclear power should be maintained because	Rating
1 it safeguards jobs in the power industry.	☐
2 it preserves expertise in nuclear technology.	☐
3 it is difficult to replace the high proportion of power generated from nuclear fuel.	☐
4 it reduces dependency on fossil fuels.	☐
5 the targets of the Kyoto Protocol will not be met if nuclear power is phased out.	☐
6 the phasing out of nuclear power is pointless as the waste produced from the past still has to be disposed of.	☐
7 it can be used as a 'bridge' until new technologies are developed in the future.	☐
8 the economy would go into recession without it because the kWh price would increase.	☐
9 the world market price of uranium is not as volatile as other fuels.	☐
10 the cost of decommissioning and dismantling plants is far too high even if energy companies have provisions for this purpose.	☐

Look at two or three websites of the main energy companies in your country.
What PR information on nuclear power do they offer? What could you add to the list above?
How does your company communicate with opponents to nuclear power?

11   Work with a partner. What counter arguments can you think of to each of those in exercise 10?
The first one is given as an example. Compare and discuss your counter arguments with the rest
of the class.

1   *Other jobs could be created if more money were invested in renewables.*

2   _____

3   _____

4   _____

5   _____

6   _____

7   _____

8   _____

9   _____

10   _____

12   **Work in groups of three. Use the information in the Partner Files to do this role-play.**

One outcome of the strategy meeting was a decision to set up training seminars aimed at helping employees respond to opponents of nuclear power. At one of the seminars, employees role-play a meeting between a chairperson (Partner A), an environmentalist (Partner B) and a representative of the energy industry (Partner C). Prepare your roles and act out the role-play.

PARTNER FILES   Partner A   File 4, p. 56
Partner B   File 10, p. 57
Partner C   File 14, p. 58

CHAIRING A MEETING

Opening the meeting
First of all, I think we should establish the overall procedure.
Can we now agree on the overall procedure?
The main objectives of the meeting are ...
Does that seem acceptable to you?

Asking somebody to start
Would you like to start, John?
John, would you like to kick off?

Keeping to the agenda
OK, could we please come back to the agenda?
I'm afraid that's not part of the discussion.

Asking for clarification
I don't quite follow. What do you mean by ... ?
I don't really get what you mean.

---

13   **Complete this puzzle with words from the unit and find the word in column a.**

1   A short-term, temporary, not permanent solution is an ... solution.
2   When you take a fossil fuel or ore from a mine, you ... it.
3   Getting rid of waste or putting it in storage is waste ... .
4   The primary fuel used in nuclear power.
5   When you stop something gradually over a period, you ... it ... . (2 words – 5, 3)
6   This is the place in the plant where nuclear fission takes place.
7   An expression which means *to comply with*, for example, a law or regulation (2 words – 6, 2)
8   We use this word to describe nuclear fuel which has been used up.
9   To decommission a plant and take it apart carefully piece by piece.

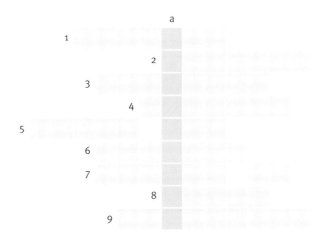

DID YOU KNOW?

The International Atomic Energy Authority (IAEA) was established in 1957 and around 140 states are members of this organization. Its main function is to promote safe, secure and peaceful use of nuclear technologies throughout the world.

OUTPUT

How do you see the future of nuclear power? Read this newspaper article about nuclear fusion and discuss the questions.

Nuclear Fusion – the Way Forward?

The challenge for the nuclear power industry is to make the technology as safe and secure as possible. After all, most people have heard of the catastrophic effects of the accident at Chernobyl in 1986 – the repercussions of which can still be seen today, with radioactive fallout

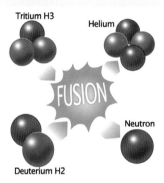

Tritium H3
Helium
FUSION
Neutron
Deuterium H2

contaminating large areas of Ukraine, Russia and Belarus. There is also the contentious issue of dealing with the waste from the nuclear fission process, which has still not been adequately dealt with in most countries.

The question arises: can such waste be avoided in the first place? Not it would seem with nuclear fission, but nuclear fusion could be the answer if it is ever successfully developed.

In this process isotopes of hydrogen – deuterium and tritium – have to be heated up to over 100 million °C. The atoms are thereby fused together thus releasing enormous amounts of thermal energy, which could then be harnessed to produce electricity. There are a number of benefits. No greenhouse gases are released, very little radioactive waste is produced – as is the case with nuclear fission – and furthermore the primary fuel is abundantly available on earth.

This technology, however, is still in its infancy. The EU, USA, China, India, Russia, Japan and South Korea have set up a project called ITER (the International Thermonuclear Experimental Reactor), which includes an experimental reactor in Cadarache, France. The goal of the project is to make fusion commercially viable. But experts say it will take at least 30 years to achieve the target and there is also no guarantee of any success.

ITER has other critics too. Some environmental groups claim that the money invested in the project – around €10 billion – should be used to develop renewable energy, firstly because it is available today and secondly because it has a proven track record. ■

OVER TO YOU

- Do you think nuclear fusion can be developed successfully? State your reasons.
- Should countries cooperate to develop new technologies concerning energy production? Give your reasons why or why not.
- Do you think the money invested in the ITER project should be spent elsewhere?
- Do you agree that renewables have a proven track record?

5 Investment plans

RTER

What factors do managers of energy companies take into account when considering a takeover? Complete the diagram, then compare and discuss your diagram with other members of your class.

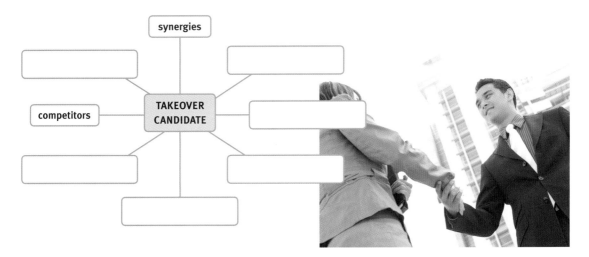

synergies

competitors

TAKEOVER CANDIDATE

What mergers or acquisitions do you know about?
How successful were they and what were the consequences?

1 **ELEC is making a takeover bid for the Scottish company, Strathclyde Energy. ELEC's PR department is monitoring the media coverage. Listen to this radio report and take notes on reactions to the bid from the following.**

1 Consumers
2 Staff
3 The British Trade and Industry minister
4 Financial analysts

2 **Complete the sentences below from the radio report. Listen again to check your answers.**

1   A lot of people will be _____ to other companies if a price increase occurs.

2   Staff in the company are deeply concerned about _____ .

3   There have been _____ made by ELEC that staff have nothing to fear.

4   The Trade and Industry Minister, Hilary Alexander, is also making sure that everything is

_____ .

5   She fears the move may _____ European competition laws.

6   It's just not _____ that large firms from abroad buy British firms.

7   Some analysts claim that the potential for _____ within a new corporate structure would be minimal.

8   They doubt whether the takeover would be a viable _____ .

9   The company is already having dificulties _____ its interests in Spain with its operations in the rest of Europe.

3 **A SWOT analysis helps a company to identify its internal strengths and weaknesses, and its external opportunities and threats. Before the takeover bid, managers at Strathclyde listed these 13 points about their firm. Sort them into the SWOT matrix.**

SWOT Analysis	
Strengths	Weaknesses
Opportunities	Threats

Now work with a partner and decide how you see your company's strengths, weaknesses, opportunities and threats. Present your findings to the rest of the class.

Items for SWOT analysis

1   Profit levels currently healthy

2   Staff morale satisfactory

3   Management structure hierarchical: means decision-making process slow

4   Good customer service, but high prices

5   Legislation from Brussels could impair operations

6   Other companies are penetrating traditional markets

7   Plans to take over one competitor; synergy effects possible

8   Number of employees relatively high for business; could be reduced

9   Core business electricity and gas

10   Gas distribution grid in need of repair

11   Good chances of further penetrating UK market

12   Regulator is monitoring company's presence in local geographical area

13   Due to profit levels, the company could become a takeover candidate

3 News of the takeover bid produced familiar reactions. Read these statements and decide who is in favour, who is against, and who is neutral.

1
If you look at takeovers and mergers in the energy business, it's always the same old story. Managers talk about shareholder value with little concern for employees who will be laid off or encouraged to take early retirement.

2
Takeovers and mergers in any industry are necessary for consolidation and investment. They enhance efficiency in the market, and uncompetitive utilities will go out of business anyway.

3
At the end of the day what do we see? Top managers get bonuses and other benefits while the consumer just gets higher prices. I think it's all bad for competition within the energy market.

4
The real problem is collusion and uncompetitive pricing. It's essential that there is the right legislation in place to stop such things. It doesn't really matter whether companies are owned and run privately or by the state.

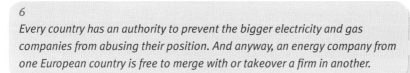

5
To be honest, I'd like Europe to return to the old set-up. Each country had one or two monopolistic utilities that really looked after all stakeholders – especially the employees and the customers.

6
Every country has an authority to prevent the bigger electricity and gas companies from abusing their position. And anyway, an energy company from one European country is free to merge with or takeover a firm in another.

Now say which statements you agree with and why.

5 Before ELEC took over Strathclyde Energy, financial statements were analysed.
Match these documents to their definitions.

☐ 1   Balance sheet
☐ 2   Profit and loss account (income statement)
☐ 3   Cash flow statement

a   This statement shows the expenditures and sales of a company over a period of time. These are balanced to give a final positive or negative figure.
b   Basically a statement which shows incoming and outgoing cash of a company during a particular period.
c   This document gives details about the financial position of a company at a particular time. It is divided into assets, equity, and liabilities.

A balance sheet lists fixed assets, current assets, equity, and liabilities.
Work with a partner and sort the following terms into these four categories.

> accounts payable (money the company owes to its suppliers) • accounts receivable (money owed to the company by its customers) • buildings • cash at the bank • company capital (owned by shareholders) • inventory • long-term financial assets • power plants • provisions •

Fixed assets: _____

Current assets: _____

Equity: _____

Liabilities: _____

Look at a copy of the most recently issued balance sheet of the company you work for (from the last annual report or the Internet). Answer these questions.

1   What fixed assets does your company have? What does the company use them for?
2   Has the value of these fixed assets gone down compared with the previous year? If so, explain why. Is it due to depreciation or to other reasons?
3   What are your company's current assets?
4   What do the inventories of the company consist of? What are they used for?
5   What is the value of your company's equity? Who owns the shares?
6   What are the provisions in your company used for?
7   Why is it important to have the provisions?

DID YOU KNOW?

ROI stands for return on investment. It is a ratio that measures the profit gained relative to the amount of money invested. It is usually expressed as a percentage and gives an indication whether a particular investment is meeting expectations.

AUDIO
11

7 After the takeover has gone through, Richard Mellor receives a phone call from his ELEC colleague, Anna. Listen to the phone call. What does Richard have to note down in his calendar?

Now listen again for the details. Answer these questions.

1 What concrete plan has Anna been given the task of implementing?
2 What will be the consequences for staff in Scotland?
3 How urgent is it to take action?
4 What's on her agenda?
5 Why does she want the meeting in Germany rather than in Scotland?

8 Work in a group of three. Use the information in the Partner Files and the language below to do this role-play.

Anna (Partner A), Richard (Partner B) and James Sinclair (Partner C) meet in Berlin. Prepare your roles and act out the role-play. Your task is to agree on a strategy.

PARTNER FILES
Partner A File 5, p. 56
Partner B File 11, p. 57
Partner C File 15, p. 58

DISCUSSION IN A MEETING

Proposing
Couldn't we just …?
What if we …?
Why don't we …?

Asking for agreement/disagreement
Do we all agree on that?
Does anybody object to this?
Who's in favour of this proposal?

Showing concern
I have some reservations/concerns about …
Actually, I don't think that's a good idea.

Emphasizing
I'd again like to point out that …
I know I keep going on about this, but …

9 Your company is following developments at ELEC closely. You find this information. Write a memo summarizing ELEC's plans.

Mixed reactions to Yorkshire plans

ELEC, the European energy group, has just announced plans to develop new coal fields in Yorkshire, England, together with the construction of a new coal-fired plant. This move has puzzled industrial analysts as it is well known that coal production is more expensive in industrialized countries than other parts of the world, mainly because of higher labour costs.

It is even more surprising given the present glut of coal on the world market and that British Coal withdrew from the area in 1990 saying that mining was no longer viable. ELEC, however, is confident that the project is a viable investment. It has forecast that the present situation will change and also stressed the fact that personnel costs in the UK are among the lowest in Western Europe. The company also maintains that it can mine coal more efficiently because of advances in extraction technology. In addition, current high prices of oil and gas mean that coal is more economically viable.

What do you think of the plan? Could it be a viable investment? Why, or why not?

10 ELEC opened a visitor centre in Yorkshire. The centre had this diagram of a coal-fired plant. Complete the gaps using words from the box, then describe the processes at the plant in your own words. Use phrases for describing a process in Unit 4, page 32.

coal crusher • coal storage area • condenser • stack • transformer • turbine •

Functional diagram of power plant process

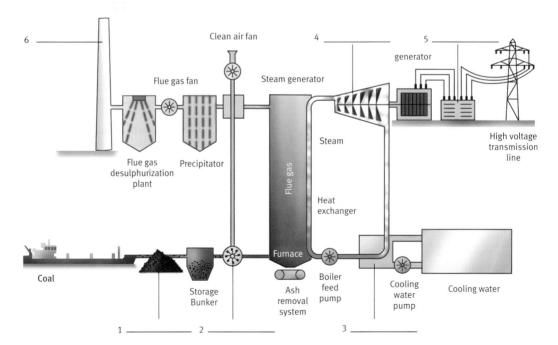

11 These headlines are taken from energy journals. Write down the first paragraph of each article and then compare and discuss your texts with other members of the class.

1
New State-of-the-Art Plant Creates 50 New Jobs

2
Energy Firms Swallow Up Municipal Utilities

3
Coal Makes a Comeback

4
Too Much Red Tape Stifles Investment

Now work with a partner and find out about one of your company's investment projects from the firm's website, annual report or other sources. Present your results to the rest of the class.

TPUT

Why do energy companies disinvest and/or sell off operations? Read this newspaper article about disinvestment and discuss the questions below.

 # Disinvestment in Europe

In a due diligence process a company wishing to take over another firm would carefully investigate all the facts and aspects of the deal before making a final decision. In the energy business, one important issue is whether the operations of a takeover candidate actually correspond to the core business of the buying company. This is not as straightforward as it may seem. Some candidates may have operations covering public transport or water supply. Subsequent investment must be contemplated as sometimes the infrastructures, such as the water-pipe systems or vehicles, may need replacing or repair. Unwanted activities could be sold off or disinvested after the takeover, but this may not always be possible or the procedures may prove to be too cumbersome.

This aspect of disinvestment is not to be underestimated. European energy companies may have to take on the mighty European Commission when drawing up their investment plans as there are moves to force companies to unbundle their divisions completely. For those involved in generation, transport and supply, it would mean selling off transmission and distribution networks to new owners and operators. All for the sake of market liberalization and transparency, it is said. Others claim it is tantamount to expropriation.

But who would invest in these grids? Some in Brussels say the taxpayer. But this would be nationalization through the backdoor, which would make a mockery of free-market policies in Europe.

OVER TO YOU

- Do you think the European Commission is right to force energy companies to sell off their grids? State your reasons.
- How does the government in your country view this?
- Do you agree with the concept of nationalization? Is it good for stakeholders (shareholders, employees and customers)?

6 The future of energy

How do you see the future? Look at the points given below and note down how you see developments over the next five years. Compare and discuss your ideas with other members of the class.

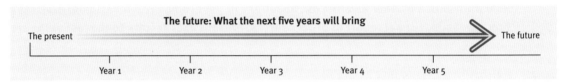

1 your own job responsibilities
2 the functions of the department you work in
3 the projections for your company's market(s)
4 the communication flow within your company
5 pay and conditions of the staff at your company
6 the core business of your firm
7 your company's image
8 innovations created or used by your company
9 the structure of your company

1 **What are the functions of the departments listed below? Match the targets to the departments.**

Departments
1 auditing
2 human resources (HR)
3 IT
4 legal services
5 public relations (PR)
6 procurement
7 research and development (R&D)
8 sales and marketing

Targets
a to acquire more industrial customers
b to be more proactive about negative media coverage
c to bundle purchase volume
d to develop a sustainable sponsorship strategy for sport and cultural events
e to establish a computer helpline for staff
f to establish benchmarks or yardsticks for an interdepartmental costing system
g to harmonize pension schemes throughout the group
h to identify inefficiencies in financial processes
i to implement new payroll processes
j to make tests in fuel-cell technology
k to reduce the number of suppliers
l to set up a loyalty-card system for retail customers
m to standardize contracts
n to upgrade software

2 **Read the following email from a manager. Does John work in the procurement, trading or auditing department?**

I am going to meet the CEO shortly as she has expressed concerns that we are still having some problems regarding accurate load planning. The accuracy of our forecasts for last year was disappointing. I would appreciate it if you could inform me of the reasons as you see them.

Regards,

John Baker

Now answer the email. Include the following points and use the expressions from the box. Each expression should be used once only.

attributable to • I am afraid • in addition • over and above this • to begin with •

1 Agree that forecasting was disappointing.
2 There was a sharp rise in consumption due to an unexpected economic upswing.
3 One power plant went out of action because of technical problems.
4 The Dutch/German interconnector was damaged at the beginning of the year.
5 Communication between departments must also be improved.

3 **At an interdepartmental meeting, ELEC employees are discussing the future of energy supply. Listen and take notes for the minutes using the headings below.**

Issues discussed

1 Long-distance electricity transmission

2 R&D department project

3 Geothermal heating

4 Hydrogen

Do you agree with the points made? Give your reasons.

4 One of the participants at the meeting attends a conference on the future of energy supply. There is a workshop on the fuel cell. Not all conference participants work on the technical side, so an information sheet has been provided. Read this sheet and complete the flow chart on page 49.

The Fuel Cell

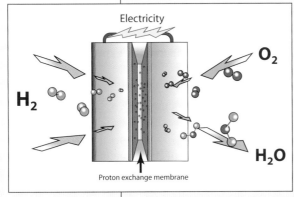

The elements of the fuel cell

The fuel cell is actually quite an old technology having been invented by the British scientist William Grove in 1843. In this apparatus, electrical power is produced in a simple yet intriguing way. As can be seen from the diagram, there are two electrodes, the anode and the cathode, and in the middle of both there is a membrane ion conductor or electrolyte. Hydrogen gas is fed continuously over the anode while oxygen from the air passes over the cathode. The electrolyte is a partition which ensures that the two gases do not come into direct contact with each other. Through the chemical process in the fuel cell, hydrogen splits into hydrogen ions and electrons. The electrons then pass through an external circuit to the cathode depicted by this glowing bulb. Electrical current is produced in this way.

The hydrogen ions meanwhile pass through the membrane. They and the electrons then react with oxygen at the cathode to produce water or steam. Thus heat is also produced, and this too can be utilized.

The electricity produced is direct current, which can be converted into alternating current if required. In order to create large volumes of power, fuel cells are connected in series to form a stack.

The beauty of the fuel cell is that the only waste product is water, although it should be stressed that the waste depends on how hydrogen is obtained to begin with. If it is derived from sources such as natural gas, CO_2 will also be produced.

Fuel cells can primarily be used in remote areas where there is no connection to the grid. But developments in this technology could mean that heat and electrical power from fuel cells will also be harnessed in the future in cities, in decentralized energy-supply systems for homes, offices and factories. We could even have them in our cellars.

So is this the key to a vision of clean, cheap, plentiful energy supply? Does it spell the end for the power plant as we know it? This is unlikely as the volumes of power needed cannot be generated by the fuel cell alone. But there will be changes, and in twenty to thirty years' time fuel cells could be common in energy supply as well as in vehicles.

1 An uninterrupted stream of _____ passes
over the anode while the _____ comes into
contact with oxygen from the air.

2 Hydrogen is divided into _____ and _____
as a result of the chemical process.

3 An _____ then conducts the
electrons to the cathode.

4 _____ pass through the membrane.

5 There is a _____ between the hydrogen
ions, electrons and oxygen at the cathode and
_____ or _____ is produced.

6 The type of electricity produced is DC (direct current), which
can be turned into _____ .

5 **How would you answer these questions in a discussion forum? Use information from the text and flow chart above, and phrases from Unit 4 page 32.**

> I still don't really understand how it works. Can you explain in simple language?

> So what exactly are the advantages, and are there any disadvantages?

> Is this the answer to all our needs? Can you produce large volumes of energy like this?

Summarize the fuel cell's advantages and disadvantages in a table.

Advantages	Disadvantages
waste mostly water or steam	depending on ...

Now summarize the advantages and disadvantages of solar panels, tidal power, fusion power or energy producing systems of your choice.

AUDIO
13

6 Delegates at the conference break for lunch. Complete this conversation using words and phrases from the box. Then listen to the dialogue and compare your version with the one on the MultiROM.

> actually • anyway • aren't they •
> by the way • getting on • really • sure •
> things • think of • to be honest •

John   Hello Steve. Good to see you again.

Steve   Hi John. How are

    _____¹?

John   Just fine. So, what did you _____

    _____² the talk on the fuel cell?

Steve   All right, but _____³ the speaker didn't really tell me anything new,

    although it was interesting.

John   _____⁴? I thought it was quite informative. _____⁵, how

    are you _____⁶ with your paper on hydrogen?

Steve   _____⁷, I'm having a few problems. It's not easy to get all the necessary

    information. Some people aren't very cooperative.

John   _____⁸? That must be quite frustrating.

Steve   Yes it is – but _____⁹. When I come to think about it, maybe you could help

    me with it. I mean, you have some good contacts.

John   _____¹⁰. How can I help?

DID YOU KNOW?

Small talk or conversation is essential in business for creating good rapport between people. It is used to build relationships, further networking, and establish a personal setting before a meeting takes place. Topics can be smaller business issues, sports, weather, etc. But subjects which are too personal should be avoided.

---

7 Work with a partner. Use the information in the Partner Files to do this role-play.

You are at a conference and, during the break, you meet a business colleague whom you have not seen for some time. Find out from your counterpart what he or she has been doing recently (work, holidays, etc). Use small-talk expressions like those in exercise 6.

PARTNER FILES   Partner A   File 6, p. 56
Partner B   File 12, p. 57

AUDIO
14

8 The conference programme contains a talk on *the hydrogen-based economy*. Look at these sentences. Do you think they are true or false?

		True	False
1	Production of hydrogen is comparatively cheap.	☐	☐
2	Greenhouse gases are avoided when hydrogen is produced via electrolysis.	☐	☐
3	The use of photovoltaic cells has no real advantage.	☐	☐
4	Storage of large quantities of the gas presents a major problem.	☐	☐
5	Hydrogen research projects are being well-funded by oil companies.	☐	☐

Now listen to the talk and check your answers.

DID YOU KNOW?

Hydrogen is the most abundant element in the universe accounting for 75% of the mass of stars and galaxies. On earth, it is found in many substances such as water or hydrocarbons, from which it can be isolated.

---

9 Your boss is expecting a report on the conference, and in particular the talk on the hydrogen economy. Write your report using the headings 1–4 and phrases from the box.
Note that you should also include your recommendations about future research at your company regarding this technology.

1 Introduction
2 Pros
3 Cons
4 Conclusions and recommendations

WRITING REPORTS

Introduction
The aim of this report is to …
This report aims to …
The objective of this report is to …

Reporting
It was pointed out that …
It was stated that …
It was established that …

Linking words
Moreover, …
Furthermore, …
However, …

Conclusions
It was concluded that …
It was agreed that …
It was decided that …

Recommendations
It is suggested that …
It is recommended that …
It is advised that …

AUDIO
15

10   **The conference is over, and the delegates are leaving. With a partner make up a dialogue in a conversational style using these prompts. Then listen to the MultiROM and compare versions.**

1   John indicates that the conference was interesting.

_____

2   Steve agrees.

_____

3   John suggests a drink at the bar.

_____

4   Steve declines – he has to catch a plane.

_____

5   John indicates disappointment; asks about Steve's arrival time at home.

_____

6   Steve gives the time; indicates he must leave now.

_____

7   John says goodbye; asks Steve to give regards to his colleague, Sonia.

_____

8   Steve responds and says goodbye.

_____

11   **Find out what research and development projects your company or a company you work with is doing. Get information from its website, annual report or other material. Present and discuss the main ones.**

12   **Complete this puzzle. What is the word in column a?**

1   *Hi! How are …? – Great, thanks.*
2   *The hydrogen economy within twenty …? I don't believe it.*
3   *How … does the water-pipe system have to be in the ground?*
4   A cable which can conduct electricity with little energy loss.
5   A place which is far away, perhaps in the middle of nowhere, is … .
6   The type of energy that you get from under the ground.
7   An apparatus invented by William Grove which produces electricity. (2 words – 4, 4)
8   An idea or picture of the future.

TPUT **Do you know if there are international projects concerning energy? Read this newspaper article and discuss the questions.**

Lack of Vision

We are all aware of the crisis concerning energy. Climate change, constantly increasing demand, depleting reserves of

primary fuels – the issues have become so familiar that we have become bored with the whole question. We are no longer prepared to listen. But the problem is not going to go away.

There seems to be a mass of short-term solutions to this long-term problem. But it is not just a question of getting on a bus and leaving the car at home, switching off lights and DVD recorders, or doing without a winter holiday. If we take a sober look at what is going on, there is a sense of something lacking. Where is the vision? This is not just a question to be put to energy companies and politicians, but to everyone. When are we going to get to grips with solving this most urgent of problems? What is needed is a change in people's long-term thinking.

Around 50 years ago, John F. Kennedy announced that the U.S.A would be able to put a man on the moon by the end of the decade. Similarly, there is now international willingness to cancel third-world debt. Why can we not create the same worldwide momentum to find new energy solutions? The hydrogen economy, fuel cells, even nuclear fusion: these are technologies which we can develop now for ourselves and for future generations.

Let's not leave the decision to the whims of the market. It is time to act now. With political will, vision, and by making a concerted effort, we can make a difference, and safeguard the livelihoods of future generations.

OVER TO YOU

- Do you agree there is a lack of vision in the energy industry? If so, what vision could be created?
- Is there a need to have international cooperation on the issue of the hydrogen-based economy? Give your reasons.

Test yourself!

See how much energy vocabulary you have learned.
Use the clues to complete the crossword puzzle.

Across

2 Another word for *repository*, e.g. for nuclear waste.
4 A ... gas like CO_2 which causes climate change.
7 The development of a price or consumption.
8 You would probably find this in your cellar; it measures energy consumption.
10 The opposite of *stable*.
11 Some energy companies plan to ... out nuclear power and then stop production.
13 To release harmful substances into water or the atmosphere.
14 Money used to finance future business risks, e.g. company pensions or dismantling power stations.
15 This is the 'marriage' of two or more companies.
16 The opposite of *weakness*.
19 Another word for *benchmark*.
22 When you have an unpaid bill or owe money to somebody, this is a ... .
23 You will find these in the balance sheet – buildings, plants, cash, etc.
26 This word describes when something is good for you.
27 A supplier of gas and electricity to customers.
28 The network of lines or pipelines.
29 This kind of plant produces both heat and electricity.
30 Everything around you, particularly the countryside, water, forests, air, etc.

Down

1 To put a power plant into operation.
3 This is the decrease in value over time of an object (e.g. network, building etc.); the word is used in accounting.
5 To modernize a power station by equipping it with new parts.
6 This is what you do to uranium so that it can be used to generate electricity.
9 This is where nuclear reactions occur.
12 A kind of brown coal.
17 In the middle of nowhere.
18 A gas which could replace fossil fuels in the future.
20 An energy company must have this attribute to be able to supply gas and electricity all the time.
21 A kind of barrier in cables and lines which is not good for the flow of electricity.
24 This is what you do to nuclear waste before it is stored long term.
25 Not voluntary, compulsory.

Partner A

Partner files

UNIT 1, EXERCISE 4   FILE 01

You work for ELEC in Spain. Phone your colleague in Britain and obtain the missing information. Help him/her with information that he/she needs.

Name of plant	Type	Load	Commissioned	Capacity	Location
Haymarket	_____	_____	_____	_____	45 km east of Birmingham, England
Glengarry	_____	_____	_____	_____	____ km south of Inverness, Scotland
Steinburg	lignite	base and intermediate loads	1965, retrofitted in 1984	3 units: Units A and B each producing 152 MW p.a.*; Unit C 284 MW p.a.	80 km north of Berlin, Germany
Brenes	natural gas	intermediate and peak load	(You don't know.)	2 units each producing 410 MW p.a.	24 km east of Seville, Spain

*p.a. = *per annum* = per year

UNIT 2, EXERCISE 12   FILE 02

You are Paul. During your conversation with Anna you should discuss the agenda and make the following points. You should make some notes about what Anna says.

- Summarize the problem, and point out that a third plant in Venlo in the Netherlands is now no longer being supplied due to the collapse of the grid.
- ELEC's progress in repairing equipment: Find out the present status.
- Make AECP's position quite clear: If the problem is not remedied soon, members will be forced to look for a new supplier. Talks about this are due to start next week.
- Loss of production: You want compensation for this.
- Future contracts: You want a cheaper price and Anna and her team should prepare some proposals for the meeting.

UNIT 3, EXERCISE 8   FILE 03

You should direct the meeting with your two colleagues. You would like to make the following proposals. Discuss these and the suggestions made by your colleagues, and decide with them on the best five.

- ELEC should focus more on renewables by building more wind generators and solar plants. They could be more economic in the long term.
- A series of seminars should be organized for ELEC staff so that they become familiar with the issues involved. They could thus become spokespersons for the company in the world outside.
- The company should start an image campaign in the media outlining positive aspects of the company.

UNIT 4, EXERCISE 12   FILE 04

You are going to chair this meeting. The two sides come from an environmentalist group and the energy industry. Your position during the discussion should be neutral although you are free to ask questions.

- Before the discussion begins, the parties will need time to prepare their arguments. During this time you could prepare a short agenda.
- After this welcome the participants to the meeting and ask them to present their points. Each should be given some time to present his or her arguments.
- Then allow time for an open discussion.
- At the end, summarize the main points and give your judgement on who was more convincing.

UNIT 5, EXERCISE 8   FILE 05

You are Anna and should chair the meeting.

- First remind the other participants that Strathclyde Energy's IT and procurement departments are to be integrated into ELEC's Shared Services Division. Stress the urgency of the project and the need to move fast.
- Ask Richard (Partner B) to outline the key issues.
- Ask James (Partner C) for his views.
- Encourage discussion, make sure the three of you reach an agreement at the end.
- Summarize the agreement.

UNIT 6, EXERCISE 7   FILE 06

Make some notes in bullet-point format about what you have done recently. This could be from your job, a special project, maybe a recent holiday, etc. You should use this information to make small talk with your partner. Find out what he or she has been doing recently. Use expressions like those in exercise 6. Remember that your objective is to make conversation.

Partner files

UNIT 1, EXERCISE 4   FILE 07

You work for ELEC in Britain. Your colleague phones from Spain. Answer his/her questions, and then ask for the information that you are missing.

Name of plant	Type	Load	Commissioned	Capacity	Location
Steinburg	_____	_____	_____	_____	80 km north of Berlin, Germany
Brenes	_____	_____	_____	_____	_____
Haymarket	nuclear	base load	1982	2 units each producing 2,300 MW p.a.*	45 km east of Birmingham, England
Glengarry	hydro	peak load	1975	2 units each producing 52,000 kw p.a.	20 km south of Inverness, Scotland

*p.a. = *per annum* = per year

UNIT 2, EXERCISE 12   FILE 08

You are Anna. During your conversation with Paul you should discuss the proposed agenda and make the following points. You should make some notes about what Paul says.

- Summarize the problem as you see it and point out that other power firms are suffering from the same problems, not just ELEC.
- ELEC's progress in repairing equipment: Reaffirm that you're doing your utmost to normalize supply, but this will take at least another four weeks.
- If AECP claims compensation for loss of production, inform Paul that an emergency fund has been set up for this purpose, primarily for residential customers. You can't say more at this stage.
- Future contracts: Point out that prices cannot change as they are very competitive and the present situation is due to force majeure.

UNIT 3, EXERCISE 8   FILE 09

You are an ELEC manager. You would like to make the following proposals at the meeting with your colleagues. Discuss these and the other suggestions made and decide with the others on the best five.

- The company should organize open days in power plants for the public.
- ELEC should join forces with its main competitors to create a common strategy on how to enhance the industry's image, particularly on environmental issues.
- ELEC should sponsor "green" events, for example gardening shows, and initiate local projects in the community to clean up rivers, establish nature trails in woods, etc.

UNIT 4, EXERCISE 12   FILE 10

You represent an environmentalist group and are going to take part in this meeting. You will now have to prepare your arguments to convince the chairperson (Partner A) that nuclear power should be phased out. Your arguments should cover aspects such as radioactivity, storage, security, etc. Your counterpart (Partner C) comes from the energy industry. Be prepared for a heated discussion.

UNIT 5, EXERCISE 8   FILE 11

You are Richard. Anna will ask you to outline the main issues. These are as follows.

- Staff will be transferred from Glasgow to Nijmegen in the Netherlands where the Shared Services Division is based.
- There will be job losses.
- Pay levels at ELEC and Strathclyde differ.
- Employees from ELEC and Strathclyde have different pension rights.

Be prepared to discuss the issues raised by James (Partner C). You have to reach a consensus.

UNIT 6, EXERCISE 7   FILE 12

Make some notes in bullet-point format about what you have done recently. This could be from your job, a special project, maybe a recent holiday, etc. You should use this information to make small talk with your partner. Find out what he or she has been doing recently. Use expressions like those in exercise 6. Remember that your objective is to make conversation.

Partner files

UNIT 3, EXERCISE 8   FILE 13

You are an ELEC manager. You would like to make the following proposals at the meeting with your colleagues. Discuss these and the other suggestions made, and decide with the others on the best five. You think the last suggestion below is the best.

- The company should offer a green tariff to customers. They could buy electricity generated only from renewable sources. It would be more expensive, however.
- The company should pay customers €10.00 towards the purchase of any electrical equipment which saves power.
- ELEC could just keep quiet and not attract attention to itself. That way the company could keep a low profile and keep out of harm's way.

UNIT 4, EXERCISE 12   FILE 14

You represent the energy industry and are going to take part in this meeting. You will now have to prepare your arguments to convince the chairperson (Partner A) that nuclear power should be maintained and developed. These arguments should cover aspects of emission control, safe storage, etc. Your counterpart (Partner B) comes from an environmentalist group. Be prepared for a heated discussion.

UNIT 5, EXERCISE 8   FILE 15

You are James Sinclair from Strathclyde Energy in Scotland. In the discussion make sure that the following points are adequately taken into account.

- You have to have a workable proposal when you announce the plan to the staff representatives in Scotland.
- Employees are nervous because they do not know what is going to happen. They fear job losses.
- Having this meeting in Berlin has raised anxiety levels. Maybe it was not such a good idea.
- Discuss the issues and reach a consensus. Make sure you agree on a signal that will help restore staff confidence.

Answer key

UNIT 1

page 5

Starter

fossil fuels	renewables	nuclear fuel
(hard) coal	wind	uranium
oil	sun	
gas	biomass	
lignite	(wood)	
	(waves)	

1 1 c 2 h 3 e 4 f 5 i 6 d 7 a
8 g 9 b

page 6

2 1 lignite
2 gas
3 base
4 intermediate/medium
5 district heating systems
6 state-of-the-art
7 1979
8 retrofitted
9 planning permission
10 spoil

3 1 h 2 e 3 f 4 d 5 b 6 g 7 c 8 a

page 7

9 electricity production
10 fossil fuels
11 base load
12 state-of-the-art equipment
13 energy mix
14 company policy
15 power station
16 district heating

page 8

5 1 d 2 b 3 c 4 a

page 9

7 a 5 connection
b 1 transmission network
c 4 facility, distribution network
d 3 municipal utility
e 2 overhead lines, supplier

page 10

8 2 (is) fed
3 is transported
4 is owned
5 are organized
6 is delivered
7 be chosen
8 have been/are liberalized
9 are also controlled
10 are increased
11 is also monitored

page 11

9 1 transmission tower
2 subsidiary
3 state
4 to monitor
5 to ensure
6 network
7 to charge

10 1 to generate
2 to transmit, transmission operator
3 to sell, seller
4 distribution, distributor
5 regulation, regulator
6 liberalization
7 to supply, supplier

8 liberalization
9 generation
10 transmission
11 regulation
12 supply
13 sales

page 12

11 1 ELEC Holding
2 ELEC Power
3 ELEC Trading
4 ELEC Shared Services
5 ELEC Transmission and Distribution
6 ELEC Trading
7 ELEC Power
8 all the divisions
9 ELEC Power
10 ELEC Regional Supply
11 ELEC Transmission and Distribution

12 1 coal
2 distributor
3 base
4 utility
5 grid operator
6 transmission
7 generator
8 trading

a customer

UNIT 2

page 15

2 1 True
2 False
3 True
4 True
5 False

Suggested answer
1 *Members of AECP*
Medium-sized chemical producers with 50 production locations in Europe, mostly in France, the Czech Republic and Benelux countries.
2 *Development of wholesale prices*
AECP is concerned that kilowatt hour prices have been volatile over the last two years. Over the last five years average procurement costs have doubled.
3 *AECP's objectives*
The chief objective is to reduce energy costs by reaching an agreement with one supplier who will

supply all the members. Security of supply is the other chief objective.

4 *Forecasts on AECP's future energy consumption*
AECP expects energy consumption to increase particularly when other companies join the organization.

5 *Next step*
We analyse AECP's consumption patterns over the last five years and make accurate forecasts.

3 Graph 1 kilowatt hour price over the past two years
Graph 2 wholesale price over last two months
Graph 3 AECP's average procurement costs over the last five years
Graph 4 AECP's expected energy consumption over the next five years

4 1 c Graph 4 3 d Graph 3
2 a Graph 2 4 b Graph 1

5 1 fluctuate
2 hit a low and then recover
3 increase steeply; *rocket, soar*
4 level off
5 fall sharply; *decrease dramatically, plummet, plunge*
6 peak and then fall back
7 fall back and then pick up again; *recover*
8 remain stable; *hold steady*
9 rise steadily; *grow*
10 decline; *dip*

page 17

6 Suggested answer
The price started at the beginning of the year at €30 per megawatt hour, but rose steeply to over €40 by March. It then fell back until the beginning of May, when it increased again, levelling off at under €50 during June. In July it fell back, but rose again in August, levelling off once again in September. In October it increased steeply, peaking at €70, but fell back again through November and into December.

7 Suggested answers
1 There was a surge in the gas price. This happened because of the harsh winter.
2 The economy picked up. This was due to an increase in high-street spending.
3 There was a reduction in turnover. This led to the cost-cutting programme.
4 There was a power cut. This happened as a result of the collapse of the grid.
5 Consumers can now choose their supplier. This happened as a result of liberalization.
6 There is a volatile political situation. This has led to uncertainty in the market.
7 More wind farms have been built. This happened as a result of financial support from the state.

page 18

8 1, 3, 6, 7
Suggested answer
AECP crisis in Netherlands
Bad weather has disrupted supply to two AECP plants in the Netherlands. They are completely cut off, and operating on back-up emergency generators

at present. Our technical staff are working to resolve the situation, but AECP has brought up the issue of security of supply and is talking about changing supplier – even though it's clearly a question of force majeure.

9 1 c 2 e 3 d 4 b 5 a

page 19

10 1 Dear Anna
2 May I remind you
3 Before writing this letter
4 I might add
5 He assured me
6 We are extremely concerned
7 I therefore suggest
8 I look forward to hearing from you
9 Yours sincerely

page 20

11 Suggested answer
Dear Paul
Thank you for your letter dated 10 April 20--. It is indeed most unfortunate that this situation has arisen. I fully understand your concern but I would like to stress that this is a case of force majeure as the weather conditions are not typical for this time of year. These are circumstances beyond our control. Nevertheless, we are taking this matter very seriously, and I would like to assure you that our engineers are making every effort to repair the grid and other equipment as fast as possible, so that we can again supply our customers with power.
I agree that it is important to discuss the situation face to face, and I look forward to meeting you at your headquarters in Rotterdam on Tuesday, April 17th 20-- at 10.00 a.m.

I'm sure our meeting will be more than satisfactory.

With kind regards,
Anna Smith

UNIT 3

page 23

1 1 It is with great pleasure
2 please see attachment
3 by invitation only
4 to get to know
5 Could you please let me know
6 I would also be grateful
7 It would be beneficial
8 Kind regards

Suggested answer
Dear Mr Al-Naimi,
Thank you very much for your kind invitation to take part in the International Forum for Energy. I would very much like to attend.
I would be grateful if you could send me the attachment about this seminar again as unfortunately it did not reach me.
During the open forum on the Thursday evening, I would like to raise the issue of biofuels and would appreciate it if you could include this on the agenda.
I look forward to hearing from you.

Kind regards,
Anna Smith

page 24

2 1 False. The public sees the industry as one of the main culprits with regard to all the major environmental problems.
2 False. Gas is the second most important source standing at 25%.
3 False. It accounts for 20%.
4 True.
5 False. It is not well known.
6 True.

page 25

3 1 greenhouse gases
2 acid rain
3 hole (in the) ozone layer
4 Carbon dioxide
5 climate change
6 emissions trading
7 air pollution
8 sea level(s)
9 desulphurization plant

page 26

4 e 1   b 2   a 3   c 4   d 5

Jane's key point was the need to lobby at a national level on the issues of emissions trading and subsidies, so that all companies can do business on the same basis.

5 I'm going to be covering...
Let me move on to ...
I'd like you to look at this pie chart.
First of all ...
That completes my overview.
Please don't hesitate to interrupt me if you have any questions.

page 28

10 1 carbon dioxide – emissions
2 sulphur dioxide – emissions
3 combined heat and power – generation
4 volts, voltage – generation, transmission, distribution
5 Union for the Co-ordination of Transmission of Electricity – transmission
6 transmission systems operator – transmission
7 distribution systems operator – distribution
8 megawatt – generation
9 kilowatt hour – consumption

11 1 capture   5 graph
2 greenhouse   6 carbon
3 subsidy   7 acid
4 renewables   8 change

a research

UNIT 4

page 30

Starter
Suggested answers
waste, health, safety, radiation, disposal, security, uranium, CO2-free

1 1 c   2 a   3 a   4 c   5 b   6 b (Calder Hall in the northwest of England)

page 31

2 1 b   2 a   3 h   4 d   5 c   6 f   7 g   8 e

page 32

3 1 control elements   4 transformers
2 steam generator   5 cooling towers
3 generator   6 condenser

page 33

5 a Firstly / First of all – d Then / After that – c the next step/stage is – b Finally

6 Suggested answers
Storage and reprocessing:
Present storage arrangements are only a short-term solution.
The waste has to be transported long distances.

Long-term disposal
The site has to be away from any natural threats.
Public resistance: people don't want a long-term facility in their backyard.
People worry about security.

page 34

7 1 f   2 h   3 e   4 d   5 a   6 c   7 b   8 g

9 waste disposal
10 interim storage
11 Spent fuel
12 reprocessing plants
13 disposal facility
14 public resistance
15 safety measures
16 government legislation

page 35

8 Suggested answer.
Dear Hiro,
You asked me to give you my thoughts on the consultants' report. First of all I'd like to say how much I agree with their point about this being a time for nuclear to grow. However, I do not agree with them about this being the end for fossil fuels. There is plenty of coal and new technology will make this a cleaner energy source than it is now. We should also remember that 'peak oil' really is a debate that experts do not agree on. While some say that the world's oil production has peaked and will decline from now on, others believe that new technology will mean that new oil fields will be found and exploited, and oil extracted from other substances such as tar sands, like they are doing in Canada.

I think that the consultants are right to mention the safety of the new generation of power plants. I think that we should really highlight this, as it is an area where the joint venture will benefit from our combined expertise and research from both Japan and Europe. ELEC and JEPCO have both done extensive work on protecting nuclear power stations from terrorist attack, which we will be able to pool, and I look forward to learning new ideas from you on how to make power stations safe from earthquake damage.

I think that it will be important to show how waste management has improved but at the same time, I feel that we should be completely honest in admitting that a totally safe long-term solution has not yet been found.

I propose setting up a meeting with lobbyists to discuss how we can pursue a uniform strategy for approaching governments.

With kind regards,
Jane

9 a 1   b 6   c 7   d 2   e 5   f 8   g 3   h 10
i 9   j 4

page 36

11 Suggested answers

2 Know-how could be developed on the basis of other generation technologies.
3 As technological standards improve in generation from renewables this should not be a problem.
4 Most fossil fuels are imported from countries such as Russia and Kuwait. They are politically stable.
5 Maybe this is correct, but the effects of nuclear waste and fallout are far worse.
6 The quantities of future nuclear waste are the problem, not what has been already produced.
7 So can other sources such as wave power. All we need is the investment in such technologies.
8 Maybe the kWh price would increase but this would not necessarily lead to a recession. It would force industrial customers to be more efficient.
9 It would become more volatile if more nuclear plants were built around the world.
10 Energy companies have been forced to set up such contingencies. There is enough money saved.

page 37

13 1 interim   6 reactor
2 extract   7 adhere to
3 disposal   8 spent
4 uranium   9 dismantle
5 phase out

a reprocess

UNIT 5

page 39

Starter
Suggested answers
profits, synergies, number of employees, sales forecasts, assets, customer structure, competitors, equity

1 Suggested answer
Consumers: worried about another price rise if the takeover goes through. Risk that people will shift to other companies.
Staff: deeply concerned about redundancies particularly at the firm's headquarters in Glasgow. Employees afraid functions will head south to head office in Birmingham.
Trade and Industry Minister, Hilary Alexander: thinks the move may infringe European competition laws. Plans to consult Brussels to check that bid conforms to European directives. Opposition to large firms from abroad buying up British utilities while there are obstacles for British companies to do the same in other countries.
Financial analysts: surprised, see potential for synergies within new corporate structure as 'minimal'. They see us as already having difficulties trying to cement our interests in Spain. They claim shareholders are 'worried'.

page 40

2 1 shifting   6 on
2 redundancies   7 synergies
3 assurances   8 investment
4 done by the book 9 cementing
5 infringe

3 Strengths 1, 2, 4 (first part), 9
Weaknesses 3, 4 (second part), 8, 10
Opportunities 7, 11
Threats 5, 6, 12, 13

page 41

4 In favour: 2, 4   Against: 1, 3, 5   Neutral: 6

page 42

5 1 c   2 a   3 b

Fixed assets: buildings, long-term financial assets, power plants
Current assets: accounts receivable, cash at the bank, inventory
Equity: company capital
Liabilities: accounts payable, provisions

page 43

7 An all-day meeting next Thursday, starting at ten, with James Sinclair from Strathclyde.

1 the plan to integrate Strathclyde Energy's IT and procurement departments into ELEC's Shared Services Division
2 Staff will be transferred, and some jobs will be lost.
3 It's very urgent because there's a lot of pressure from above.
4 how to proceed with the integration and the job losses, how to harmonize pay conditions and pensions
5 to show that the decision-making process rests at ELEC's headquarters in Germany

page 44

9 Suggested answer
I found the following information on ELEC's plans. They want to develop new coal fields and construct a new coal-fired power plant in Yorkshire. With oil and gas prices on the increase, they expect the present coal glut situation will change, and that a combination of lower UK personnel costs and advances in extraction technology will make the project viable.

10 1 coal storage area   4 turbine
2 coal crusher   5 transformer
3 condenser   6 stack

UNIT 6

page 46

1
1 f, h
2 g, i,
3 e, n
4 m
5 b, d
6 c, k
7 j
8 a, l

page 47

2 John works in the trading department.

Suggested answer for the email
John
I am afraid I have to agree with you that our forecasting was disappointing. This was attributable to a number of reasons. To begin with there was a sharp rise in consumption due to an unexpected economic upswing. Then one of ELEC's power plants went out of action. In addition we had problems with the Dutch/German interconnector, which was damaged at the beginning of the year. But over and above these external reasons there was a more general problem of poor communication between departments. In my view this must be improved if we are to make accurate forecasts.

Regards (Name)

3 Suggested answer
1 Long-distance electricity transmission: need could decrease because of trend away from centralized energy systems and towards smaller power stations nearer consumption centres
2 R&D department project: superconductors as means of reducing resistance and energy losses in the grid. Biggest problem is cooling lines.
3 Geothermal heating: Water pipes under ground in back garden to harness heat! Small-scale development, and how does the company come in?
4 Hydrogen: Could be really major new development in generating electricity and fuelling transport. But are scientists' claims that hydrogen can replace fossil fuels in the foreseeable future realistic?

page 49

4
1 hydrogen gas, cathode
2 ions, electrons
3 external circuit
4 Hydrogen ions
5 reaction, water, steam
6 AC (alternating current)

5 Suggested answer
Advantages
waste mostly water or steam
can be used in remote areas and vehicles
suitable for decentralized energy supply systems
Heat can also be harnessed.
Disadvantages
depending on how hydrogen is obtained, e.g. from natural gas, CO_2 also produced
cannot produce large volumes of power such as can be generated by a power plant

page 50

6
1 things
2 think of
3 to be honest
4 Really?
5 By the way
6 getting on
7 Actually
8 Aren't they
9 anyway
10 Sure

page 51

8
1 False
2 True
3 False
4 True
5 False

9 Suggested answer
Report on the talk about the hydrogen economy
Introduction
The aim of this report is to sum up the main points of the talk given on the subject of the hydrogen economy at the ... conference on ... (date), and to make recommendations for future action.

Pros
It was stated that there are a number of advantages. If hydrogen is produced via the electrolysis of water with photovoltaic cells then the production of greenhouse gases can be avoided. It was also pointed out that hydrogen could be used instead of hydrocarbons in modified vehicle and aircraft engines. Moreover, the gas could be used together with fuel cells in cars, trucks etc. In addition, fuel cells could be used in decentralized energy systems for electricity production.

Cons
It was established that the biggest drawback is the storage of gas as very large pressurized containers would be necessary both in vehicles and elsewhere. There would also be a weight problem. The speaker pointed out that in his view governments and oil companies are reluctant to invest in the hydrogen economy.

Conclusions and recommendations
It was concluded by our team that the commercial viability of hydrogen as a future energy source is at present unclear. However, it is recommended that our company should invest more into R&D in this area. The technology could offer considerable opportunities for company growth in the future.

page 52

12
1 things
2 years
3 deep
4 superconductor
5 remote
6 geothermal
7 fuel cell
8 vision

a hydrogen

TEST YOURSELF!

page 54

Across	Down
2 storage	1 to commission
4 greenhouse	3 depreciation
7 pattern	5 retrofit
8 meter	6 enrich
10 volatile	9 reactor
11 phase	12 lignite
13 pollute	17 remote
14 provisions	18 hydrogen
15 merger	20 reliability
16 strength	21 resistance
19 yardstick	24 reprocess
22 liability	25 mandatory
23 assets	
26 beneficial	
27 utility	
28 grid	
29 chp	
30 environment	

Transcripts

UNIT 1, EXERCISE 2

2

Maria ELEC Public Relations, Maria Berger speaking. How can I help you?

Colin Oh hello, this is Colin Maitland. If you remember we spoke a few days ago...

Maria Yes, yes of course. Hello, Colin. How are you?

Colin Fine, thanks. And you?

Maria Fine, thanks. So what can I do for you today?

Colin Well, as I explained last time, I'm writing this series of articles on European utilities and I'd like to include ELEC in my reports.

Maria Yes, as I said, I'm happy to give you all the support I can. Where would you like to start?

Colin Well, first I'd like some general information, and I was wondering if you could outline ELEC's energy mix first of all.

Maria Sure. Well, we have a number of fossil fuels which we use for electricity production – we mostly burn lignite and gas.

Colin Right.

Maria Yes, and our lignite-fired plants are used for base load while the gas-fired ones cater for the intermediate, or medium, and peak load ranges.

Colin Mm, OK I've got that.

Maria Then we have a number of gas plants which are combined heat and power plants; we use them to generate electricity and also to supply district heating systems.

Colin Sorry, I didn't quite catch that, what sort of systems?

Maria District heating systems.

Colin Ah, yes.

Maria So those are the fossil fuel plants. Then we also have some nuclear plants which are also needed for base load.

Colin I see. Now what about the issue of emissions? I mean, the burning of fossil fuels produces these harmful emissions and environmental problems that people of course are very much aware of these days. Could you outline your company policy on this?

Maria We take this issue very seriously indeed. All our plants are fitted with state-of-the-art equipment to reduce harmful effects on the environment.

Colin Can you give me some exact figures?

Maria I'm afraid I can't help you there, but why don't I take you round one of our plants? You could then see exactly what we do.

Colin Yes, that would be great. Um, you have a number of power stations in your portfolio. What's the largest one?

Maria Well, in terms of installed capacity that would be Altrath near Berlin. It has four 600-megawatt units and can produce enough electricity to meet the needs of some two million people.

Colin I read up on that. It's relatively old, isn't it?

Maria Well, it was commissioned in 1979, but it's been retrofitted since then. Most of our other plants came on line in the 1980s and 1990s.

Colin What about wind?

Maria We're building more wind power stations although they are still quite controversial. It can be difficult to get planning permission in some countries. Not everyone is in favour of them as they say they spoil the countryside and create too much noise if you live near them.

Colin And what's your view on this?

Maria We believe these claims to be exaggerated.

UNIT 1, EXERCISE 11

3

Maria So you got the information about our power plants all right, did you?

Colin Yes, thank you. Your two colleagues were very helpful.

Maria Good. But now you'd like to know more about the structure of the company.

Colin That's right.

Maria OK. Well, this chart shows the overall set-up, and as you can see, ELEC has an unbundled structure. There's a holding company, ELEC Holding, with five divisions which are all active on the pan-European electricity and gas markets.

Colin Does that mean the divisions are companies in their own right?

Maria Yes, that's right, they are. On the far left here we have ELEC Power, which is our mining and generation division. Because, you see, in addition to our power plants we also have a number of opencast mines.

Colin OK, I didn't realize that.

Maria Yes, they produce lignite and coal, mostly in central Europe. ELEC Power also procures gas for the purposes of electricity generation from our partners in Russia and other countries.

Colin Russia, I see.

Maria Mm. But the next division is more focussed on western Europe. That's ELEC Transmission and Distribution, which has a large number of networks in Germany, Denmark, the UK, the Benelux countries, the Czech Republic, Slovakia and Spain, yes they're the main ones.

Colin But not all.

Maria No, by no means all. We are in fact in the process of consolidating this division under one management structure.

Colin Right.

Maria Then next is ELEC Trading, which is the youngest member of the ELEC family. This division procures large volumes of gas and electricity for our regional supply company – as well as for industrial companies and other utilities.

Colin So this is basically a buying operation.

Maria Yes, ELEC Trading's objective is to purchase these commodities at the cheapest price.

Colin OK. And the next division is ELEC Regional Supply, I see.

Maria Yes, it's called 'Regional', but in fact this is a Europe-wide operation. ELEC Regional Supply has a lot of subsidiaries each responsible for a confined geographical area. In this way we ensure customer proximity.

Colin A sound principle.

Maria Mm. Then finally, here on the far right, you can see the ELEC Shared Services division. This provides IT, human resources and legal services for the whole group.

UNIT 2, EXERCISE 2

Paul As I said on the phone, our association AECP represents a number of medium-sized chemical producers in Europe. We've recently pooled our requirements and set up an energy procurement unit to look into ways of reducing energy costs. I'm sure you know our industry depends on large inexpensive volumes of power to remain competitive. I mean kilowatt hour prices were very volatile over the last two years.

Anna Yes, but the wholesale price has remained stable over the last two months.

Paul That's true but we'd like to ensure that prices don't fluctuate again – at least for our members.

Anna Yes, I understand. How big is your organization?

Paul At the moment there are fifty medium-sized production locations in Europe, mostly in France, the Czech Republic and the Benelux countries, and we're looking for one supplier that can provide power for all of them.

Anna Well, that shouldn't pose any problems. What's the present situation for your members? I imagine they have contracts with local suppliers.

Paul That's right. But there's a big difference in the conditions that each one offers. And the average procurement costs have doubled over the last five years, standing at around eighteen cents per kilowatt hour now.

Anna What's your price target?

Paul Before I mention that I'd also like to emphasize that security of supply must be of a very high standard. We just can't afford breaks in transmission. We'd also insist on good customer service with one ELEC key account manager responsible for the whole contract in Europe. That person would be our contact for all countries in which we operate. That covers our main objectives.

Anna With one contact at AECP?

Paul That's right.

Anna I'm sure we could offer something that would go along those lines but prices would depend on amounts supplied and the contract period.

Paul Well, energy consumption is sure to grow over the next few years, particularly when our organization expands. Other medium-sized companies are waiting to join.

Anna OK, I suggest then that ELEC looks into your overall consumption patterns over the last five years. That way we could make some accurate forecasts.

Paul Sounds good. We should start this process as soon as possible.

UNIT 2, EXERCISE 8

Marten We've got a real crisis on our hands, Anna.

Anna Oh, what's up?

Marten It's about that new international contract we have with the Association of European Chemical Producers. Our transmission grid's gone down in the Netherlands. It's due to the weather; the system has been affected by snow and ice and some of the transmission towers have collapsed. We've got teams out there working on repairs but it's going to take a while.

Anna OK, who's affected?

Marten There are two AECP production sites affected. They're totally cut off.

Anna OK, but surely we can compensate by feeding more power in from Germany through the interconnector for the time-being. I mean, we can use third-party access using another network.

Marten Well, it's not as simple as that, I'm afraid.

Anna Why not?

Marten The Dutch-German interconnector is also out of action. This means we can't supply the plants at all at the moment.

Anna So, how are they getting power?

Marten They've switched on back-up generators but it's only a temporary solution.

Anna Mm, I see. There are bound to be questions of liability and insurance. But it's obviously a case of force majeure.

Marten Yes, well I've been in touch with our contact at AECP, Paul Robben. He's very concerned about the situation to say the least and is worried about security of supply to all of the other production facilities in other countries, not only in the Netherlands. He says all AECP members see this development as very worrying and are thinking about looking for a new agreement with another supplier.

Anna OK. I'll get in touch with him as soon as possible to reassure him. I'm sure we'll sort it out somehow.

UNIT 3, EXERCISE 4

Jane Let me once more welcome you to the tenth International Forum for Energy. I'm going to be covering a number of issues in my talk, but please don't hesitate to interrupt me if you have any questions.

Let's start with the problem of the environment. There is room for improvement here, particularly if we consider that coal and gas account for most of our generating capacity, as is outlined in the forum brochure, which I'm sure you've all read. I'd like you to look at this pie chart which illustrates the point.

So, what about our company strategy regarding the future? As you know, our intention is to build more wind, hydro and clean coal plants. But in my view such programmes are not the main issue, and so let me move on to the more crucial questions. We need to undertake a number of measures. First of all, we need to lobby governments at a national level on the key issues of emissions trading and subsidies. The aim must be that all energy companies are able to do business within the same framework, and that the industry becomes more transparent as a whole. I'm convinced that we should be more proactive in influencing legislation made by national governments. If this is done then we can develop a clearer and more cohesive future strategy and vision. That completes my overview, and I'd now like to go into the various questions in more detail. First let's take a look at …

UNIT 3, EXERCISE 6

Man My name is Frank Rice and I'm in ELEC's generating division. In this talk I want to give you an outline of what we're doing in the areas of emissions trading and research. I'll start by summarizing how emissions trading works. Many of you will be well aware of the processes involved, but for those managers and staff working in the non-related divisions this is how it works.

First of all, the general target is to reduce pollution, and to do this there are certain limits that we as power companies must stick to when it comes to the volume of greenhouse gases we can emit. We are allocated certain credits or allowances by governments; these allowances mean emissions must not exceed certain levels. Emissions trading is used when a power company gets into the situation that it exceeds the limits just outlined. The company must then buy credits from a company that pollutes less. If there's more demand, the price for these allowances increases of course, so it becomes a market in itself. ELEC has been at the forefront of this process for a number of years now.

If I could now turn to research, I'd like to outline some of the ways in which our company intends to reduce emissions. The first is carbon capture. Here, carbon dioxide is collected and then pumped deep underground, thus preventing it from reaching the atmosphere. But we are also working with specialist engineering firms to design power plant equipment that will cut CO_2 emissions to almost zero. This technology's still at the research stage but it's hoped to have such a plant in operation in the next five to seven years.

Now, if you have any questions at this point I'll …

UNIT 4, EXERCISE 3

Guide Firstly I'd like to welcome you all on behalf of ELEC. Today I'll be showing you round one of our pressurized water reactors. This is the technology you use in your JEPCO 5 plant, isn't it?

Mr Takayashi Yes, that's right, though the majority of our plants use boiling water reactors. As the next generation of power stations will be based on pressurized water technology, we felt that we could learn a lot by visiting an older version, such as this one, so that we can study where improvements can be made.

Guide OK, I'll talk you through the basics using this diagram on the screen and then we can decide which features you would like to look at more closely. If you look first at the left-hand side of the diagram, you can see the reactor pressure vessel which produces heat from nuclear fission. This occurs in the reactor core where the fuel assemblies are situated – they contain the actual uranium. Above these assemblies you can see the control elements. When these are fully lowered, nuclear fission is completely interrupted, the plant therefore operates at maximum output when they're withdrawn. All this is monitored and controlled by our expert teams in the central control rooms.

Now, it's important to realize that pressurized water reactors have two water circuits – the primary and secondary circuit, which are completely separated from each other. This prevents radiation from escaping, and so that's why they are relatively safe. In the first circuit, water transports the heat produced by nuclear fission in a closed circuit to the steam generator, where the heat is then transferred to the secondary circuit. So in the steam generator, heat from the primary circuit turns water of the secondary circuit into steam. This steam, I'd like to stress again, is totally non-radioactive due to the separation of the circuits. Any questions so far?

Mr Takayashi Yes, erm, how many fuel assemblies are there in the reactor?

Guide There are 193. Any more questions? No? OK, so the steam produced in the steam generator passes to and drives the turbine. This is connected to the generator which actually produces the electricity. From there the electricity is fed into the transformers, which raise voltage levels to the required 380 kV. Now, if you look below the box with the turbine and the generator, you can see the condenser. In this part of the plant, cooling water is used to transform the steam of the secondary circuit back to a liquid state. In a sense the cooling water forms a third circuit, but we don't in fact call it that. Anyway, this cooling water in the condenser transforms the steam of the secondary circuit back to water, which is then pumped back to the steam generator. The cooling water on the other hand can be discharged back into the river which you saw nearby the plant, or it's fed into the cooling towers. This depends on the level of the water's temperature.

Mr Tagayashi Excuse me, what's the output of the plant?

Guide The net output amounts to some 1,330 MW. Now, if you'll follow me …

UNIT 4, EXERCISE 6

Fiona OK, well before we can start formulating our own strategy on waste disposal, we would like to hear how JEPCO is dealing with this issue and see what we can learn. Mr Takayashi has kindly agreed to talk us through their plans for the future. To start with, could you, Mr Takayashi, give us a rundown of what the key issues are?

Mr Takayashi Sure. Well, the first issue is the initial and interim storage of the high-level radioactive waste, and then we have reprocessing. For our purposes we can take these together. What happens at the moment, after the fuel is extracted from the reactor, is that the waste is initially stored next to power plants. There are a number of sites where interim storage of the spent fuel is possible, but this is of course no long-term solution, and eventually the fuel has to be treated at a reprocessing plant, such as Sellafield or La Hague. This has been a major problem for the public relations of our industry, especially from the Japanese point of view. Transporting our waste over long distances to these plants does not look good. Fortunately, we have now built a reprocessing plant here in Japan, in Rokkasho in Aomori prefecture. This should go some way towards improving our image worldwide. But after reprocessing, waste still has to be transported again to where it is stored long term.

Marita So if I can summarize that, we have two problems: First the fact that the way we store waste at the moment is only a short-term measure, and then the problem of transport.

Mr Takayashi Right. But of course the really major challenge is what happens to the reprocessed fuel long term. We really do require a disposal facility for final storage.

Marita What would that entail?

Mr Takayashi Well, safety measures would require the waste to be buried deep underground away from any natural threats such as earthquakes – a big problem in Japan – and the like. I mean, the waste would be vitrified, but that wouldn't make it any less radioactive of course, but it would be more confined and compressed so that the danger of leakages would diminish. And it would then be buried under clay or granite.

Fiona And it's this question of final storage where there's most public resistance.

Mr Takayashi Yes, absolutely. Nobody wants anything like that in their backyard. In Japan we are currently working hard to identify suitable sites for burial.

Marita Security of course is also an issue for a lot of people. I mean they hear stories of uranium being stolen and are afraid this could happen anywhere.

Mr Takayashi Well, we of course have security teams at all our nuclear stations and storages to guard against any terrorist attack, as specified by government legislation. These security measures are very thorough and are strictly adhered to.

Fiona Yes, sure. And the next generation of nuclear reactors are being built to even stricter security regulations. Mr Takayashi, I would like to thank ...

UNIT 5, EXERCISE 1

10

Journalist Strathclyde Energy was in the headlines last month for putting up its bills. Today it's back in the limelight as the multi-national energy company, ELEC, makes a takeover bid for the Scottish firm. Consumers are worried about another hike in prices if the takeover goes through. Here's Gareth Macleod of the Consumers' Association.

Gareth Well, a lot of people will be shifting to other companies if a price increase occurs because of a takeover. We saw it happen in the past in other parts of the UK and so it would be no surprise if it happened here.

Journalist Staff in the company are also deeply concerned about redundancies, particularly at the firm's headquarters in Glasgow. ELEC's UK head office is based in Birmingham, and employees fear that functions will head south although there have been assurances made by ELEC that staff have nothing to fear. The Trade and Industry minister, Hilary Alexander, is also making sure that everything is done by the book. She fears the move may infringe European competition laws.

Hilary Yes, I'll be consulting Brussels to seek assurances that this move is above board and conforms to European directives. It's just not on that large firms from abroad start buying up British utilities while there are obstacles for our companies to do the same in other countries.

Journalist ELEC's move to take over Strathclyde has surprised financial analysts: some claim that the potential for synergies within a new corporate structure would be minimal and they doubt whether a takeover would be a viable investment. The company is already having difficulties cementing its interests in Spain with its operations in the rest of Europe, a fact which worries a lot of shareholders.

UNIT 5, EXERCISE 7

Anna Now, as you know, Richard, there have been a number of takeovers recently, and the board is pushing for consolidation throughout the group. One of the plans is to integrate Strathclyde Energy's IT and procurement departments into our Shared Services Division in Nijmegen.

Richard Right. That'll entail transferring staff away from the Glasgow offices then. Has the relevant trade union in the UK been notified yet?

Anna No, and that's where we expect some problems. You see, the move will also involve some job losses. But the point is we've got to start work on this straightaway; there's a lot of pressure from above. I've arranged a meeting here for next Thursday with the responsible manager at Strathclyde, James Sinclair, to discuss rolling out the project. It'll be all day, starting at ten.

Richard OK, so what's on your agenda?

Anna Well, firstly of course how we go about this integration and the job losses, but then there are questions about the staff that will be retained. One issue, you see, is that ELEC's pay levels are, on the whole, more generous than those at Strathclyde, and overall working conditions of the staff better. We have to decide what to do about those people that move to the Shared Services Division. Do we have to make changes? There's also the aspect of company pension rights.

Richard OK, I'm with you.

Anna That's why we need to have this meeting with James. I'm hoping he'll help us find solutions that are good for the company and acceptable to the staff. It's clear we're going to have to tread carefully; Strathclyde has a long history as an independent company. Its employees won't like these new and sudden developments, particularly if they feel their job is jeopardized.

Richard Yes, I know. But why are you planning to have the meeting here? Wouldn't it offer a positive signal if we met James in Glasgow?

Anna I've thought hard about that, but it's more important to set a signal that the decision-making process rests here at our headquarters in Germany.

Richard Ah, OK.

UNIT 6, EXERCISE 3

Anna Yes, that's right but there are also other very interesting new developments in that area. We've been monitoring for some time what seems to be the beginning of a local energy approach, with cities across Europe wanting to break away from centralized energy systems. There are already some concrete plans to build smaller power stations in the vicinity of consumption, which would reduce the need for long-distance electricity transmission.

Mark Transmission issues are certainly something that should be on the agenda. One development that R&D is looking at is how to reduce resistance and energy losses in the grid system through the use of superconductors. At the moment, the biggest problem is cooling the lines and cables to very low temperatures, which is expensive.

John And calls into question whether it'll ever be commercially viable.

Mark Sure. But it's something we mustn't lose sight of.

John No, no, of course. But going back for a moment to the movement towards local energy that Anna was talking about, there's also this trend towards harnessing geothermal energy by putting water-pipe systems a few metres below the surface of the ground.

Mark Dig a hole in your back garden and that's the end of your energy problems!

John Well, underground ambient temperatures are pretty stable at around eight to ten degrees centigrade, and the idea that you can install your own system and save on heating costs is very attractive to home owners. I mean, as a consumer I'd certainly think of doing it.

Robin Yes, but where do we as a company come in? And besides, that's more a small-scale thing. What we really need to be looking at is the big scale, and I'm surprised nobody's mentioned hydrogen yet. I mean we've been talking for a long time about hydrogen replacing fossil fuels, but there are now scientists out there claiming that this really is just round the corner and that we'll be filling up our cars with hydrogen instead of gas, or petrol as you guys say, within the next ten to twenty years, I mean in addition to using it to generate electricity.

Anna Yes, I know, but I mean, isn't that ...

UNIT 6, EXERCISE 6

John Hello Steve. Good to see you again.

Steve Hi John. How are things?

John Just fine. So, what did you think of the talk on the fuel cell?

Steve All right, but to be honest the speaker didn't really tell me anything new, although it was interesting.

John Really? I thought it was quite informative. By the way, how are you getting on with your paper on hydrogen?

Steve Actually, I'm having a few problems. It's not easy to get all the necessary information. Some people aren't very cooperative.

John Aren't they? That must be quite frustrating.

Steve Yes it is, but anyway. Come to think of it, maybe you could help me with it. I mean you have some good contacts.

John Sure. How can I help?

UNIT 6, EXERCISE 8

Speaker So welcome back. I hope you had a good lunch and are ready for an exciting new topic, because now I'd like to move onto the issue of the hydrogen economy.

As I'm sure you know, some universities are undertaking R&D into finding a substitute for fossil fuel. Hydrogen seems to be the best candidate although at present production is quite expensive. The gas can be obtained from fossil fuels such as natural gas, but in this process CO_2 is released, which is not beneficial. Research is therefore focussed on producing hydrogen from water via electrolysis because the production of greenhouse gases can be avoided in this way. The only products are oxygen and hydrogen. One of the most interesting ways of doing this is to use photovoltaic cells. The current generated from these cells could be used for the purpose of electrolysis.

If we move on now to the possible applications, hydrogen could be used in a number of ways instead of hydrocarbons. Aircraft engines could be modified to burn the fuel. Road vehicles could also burn hydrogen in internal combustion engines with certain technical changes. The big advantage, again, would be that the combustion process produces no greenhouse gases. Hydrogen could also be utilized to power vehicles with electric motors in conjunction with fuel cells. And, again in combination with fuel cells, hydrogen could be harnessed for electricity production in decentralized energy systems.

Storage of the gas, however, is one of the biggest challenges. It can be stored in pressurized containers, but the problem is that the quantities needed for practical application are very large when compared with the fuels we use today. This is particularly true for vehicles and aircraft. Weight would also pose a problem. But perhaps the biggest obstacle for this technology is the reluctance of governments and oil companies to support research. So it would seem that whether the hydrogen economy ever becomes a reality will depend on the market.

UNIT 6, EXERCISE 10

John Well, that was an interesting conference, wasn't it?

Steve Yes, it was.

John So, how about a drink at the bar?

Steve Well, I'm afraid I have to catch my plane. I'm pressed for time.

John That's a shame. What time do you think you'll be getting back home?

Steve Around midnight if all goes well. So, look, I've got to go. It was good to see you again.

John Likewise. Well, see you around. Oh, by the way, give my regards to Sonia.

Steve I'll do that. OK, see you.

A–Z word list

		Translation			Translation
A	abbreviation [ə,bri:vi'eɪʃn]		**B**	back-up ['bæk ʌp]	
	abundant [ə'bʌndənt]			balance sheet ['bæləns ʃi:t]	
	abundantly [ə'bʌndəntli]			base load ['beɪs ləʊd]	
	to abuse [ə'bju:z]			beforehand [bɪ'fɔ:hænd]	
	access ['ækses]			behalf: on ~ of	
	to account for [ə'kaʊnt fə]			[ɒn bɪ'hɑ:f əv]	
	accurate ['ækjərət]			benchmark ['bentʃmɑ:k]	
	acid rain [,æsɪd 'reɪn]			beneficial [,benɪ'fɪʃl]	
	to acquire [ə'kwaɪə]			benefit ['benɪfɪt]	
	acquisition [,ækwɪ'zɪʃn]			beyond one's control	
	acronym ['ækrənɪm]			[bɪ,jɒnd wʌnz kən'trəʊl]	
	action: out of ~			bid [bɪd]	
	[,aʊt əv 'ækʃn]			binding ['baɪndɪŋ]	
	to address sth [ə'dres]			bound: to be ~ to be	
	to adhere to sth [əd'hɪə tə]			[bi 'baʊnd tə]	
	to adopt [ə'dɒpt]			to brainstorm ['breɪnstɔ:m]	
	adverse ['ædvɜ:s]			break [breɪk]	
	to affect [ə'fekt]			breakdown ['breɪkdaʊn]	
	agency ['eɪdʒənsi]			bubble ['bʌbl]	
	agenda [ə'dʒendə]			to bundle ['bʌndl]	
	agreement [ə'gri:mənt]			to bury ['beri]	
	aim [eɪm]			by the way [baɪ ðə 'weɪ]	
	air [eə]				
	to allocate ['æləkeɪt]		**C**	campaign [kæm'peɪn]	
	allowance [ə'laʊəns]			to cancel ['kænsl]	
	along those lines			to cap [kæp]	
	[ə,lɒŋ ðəʊz 'laɪnz]			capture ['kæptʃə]	
	to alter ['ɔ:ltə]			carbon ['kɑ:bən]	
	alternating ['ɔ:ltəneɪtɪŋ]			carbon dioxide	
	alternatively [ɔ:l'tɜ:nətɪvli]			[,kɑ:bən daɪ'ɒksaɪd]	
	aluminium [,æljə'mɪniəm]			carbon footprint	
	ambassador [æm'bæsədə]			[,kɑ:bən 'fʊtprɪnt]	
	ambient ['æmbiənt]			catastrophic [,kætə'strɒfɪk]	
	amendment [ə'mendmənt]			to catch [kætʃ]	
	amount [ə'maʊnt]			to cater for ['keɪtə]	
	Anglo-Saxon [,æŋgləʊ 'sæksn]			cathode ['kæθəʊd]	
	annual ['ænjuəl]			to cement [sɪ'ment]	
	anode ['ænəʊd]			CEO [,si: i: 'əʊ]	
	apparatus [,æpə'reɪtəs]			chairperson ['tʃeəpɜ:sn]	
	to appoint [ə'pɔɪnt]			challenge ['tʃæləndʒ]	
	to appreciate [ə'pri:ʃieɪt]			changeover ['tʃeɪndʒəʊvə]	
	approach [ə'prəʊtʃ]			chart [tʃɑ:t]	
	to approach [ə'prəʊtʃ]			to check [tʃek]	
	to arise [ə'raɪz]			chemical ['kemɪkl]	
	to associate [ə'səʊʃieɪt]			circuit breaker	
	association [ə,səʊsi'eɪʃn]			['sɜ:kɪt breɪkə]	
	assurance [ə'ʃʊərəns]			circumstance ['sɜ:kəmstəns]	
	to assure [ə'ʃʊə]			to claim [kleɪm]	
	attachment [ə'tætʃmənt]			to clarify ['klærəfaɪ]	
	attention [ə'tenʃn]			clay [kleɪ]	
	attributable: to be ~ to sth			client ['klaɪənt]	
	[bi ə'trɪbjətəbl tə]			co-ordination [kəʊ,ɔ:dɪ'neɪʃn]	
	auditing ['ɔ:dɪtɪŋ]			coal: hard ~ [hɑ:d 'kəʊl]	
	automotive [,ɔ:tə'məʊtɪv]			coal-fired [,kəʊl'faɪəd]	
	availability [ə,veɪlə'bɪləti]			cohesive [kəʊ'hi:sɪv]	
	aware: to be ~ [bi ə'weə]			collapse [kə'læps]	
	axis ['æksɪs]				

Translation

collusion [kə'luːʒn]
combustion [kəm'bʌstʃn]
to come into effect
   [ˌkʌm ɪntuː ɪ'fekt]
commercial [kə'mɜːʃl]
to commission [kə'mɪʃn]
to commit [kə'mɪt]
commodity [kə'mɒdəti]
comparatively
   [kəm'pærətɪvli]
competition [ˌkɒmpə'tɪʃn]
competitiveness
   [kəm'petətɪvnəs]
competitor [kəm'petɪtə]
complaint [kəm'pleɪnt]
to comply with
   [kəm'plaɪ wɪð]
compressed [kəm'prest]
to comprise [kəm'praɪz]
concern [kən'sɜːn]
concerned: to be ~
   [bi kən'sɜːnd]
concerted [kən'sɜːtɪd]
condenser [kən'densə]
condition [kən'dɪʃn]
conditions [kən'dɪʃnz]
to conduct [kən'dʌkt]
conductor [kən'dʌktə]
confined [kən'faɪnd]
connection [kə'nekʃn]
consequence ['kɒnsɪkwəns]
to conserve [kən'sɜːv]
to consider [kən'sɪdə]
to consolidate [kɒn'sɒlɪdeɪt]
construction [kən'strʌkʃn]
consultant [kən'sʌltənt]
to consume [kən'sjuːm]
consumer [kən'sjuːmə]
consumption [kən'sʌmpʃn]
contact ['kɒntækt]
to contaminate
[kən'tæmɪneɪt]
to contemplate
   ['kɒntəmpleɪt]
contentious [kən'tenʃəs]
continuously [kən'tɪnjuəsli]
contract ['kɒntrækt]
controversial [ˌkɒntrə'vɜːʃl]
conversational
   [ˌkɒnvə'seɪʃənl]
convinced of [kən'vɪnst əv]
core [kɔː]
corporate ['kɔːpərət]
to correspond to sth
   [ˌkɒrɪ'spɒnd tə]
cost-cutting ['kɒstkʌtɪŋ]
costing ['kɒstɪŋ]
counter ['kaʊntə]
counterpart ['kaʊntəpɑːt]
to cover ['kʌvə]
credit ['kredɪt]
criticism ['krɪtɪsɪzəm]
crucial ['kruːʃl]
to crush [krʌʃ]

Translation

culprit ['kʌlprɪt]
cumbersome ['kʌmbəsəm]
current ['kʌrənt]
current assets
   [ˌkʌrənt 'æsets]

D to deal with ['diːl wɪð]
debt [det]
decision-making
   [dɪ'sɪʒn meɪkɪŋ]
to decline [dɪ'klaɪn]
to decommission
   [ˌdiːkə'mɪʃn]
to decrease [dɪ'kriːs]
delighted: to be ~
   [bi dɪ'laɪtɪd]
demand [dɪ'mɑːnd]
denox [dɪ'nɒks]
to depend on [dɪ'pend ɒn]
to deplete [dɪ'pliːt]
deposit [dɪ'pɒzɪt]
depreciation [dɪˌpriːʃi'eɪʃn]
to derive [dɪ'raɪv]
desulphurization
   [diːˌsʌlfəraɪ'zeɪʃn]
diligence ['dɪlɪdʒəns]
to diminish [dɪ'mɪnɪʃ]
direct debit [dəˌrekt 'debɪt]
direct current
   [daɪrekt 'kʌrənt]
director [də'rektə]
to discharge [dɪs'tʃɑːdʒ]
to disinvest [ˌdɪsɪn'vest]
to dismantle [dɪs'mæntl]
dismayed [dɪs'meɪd]
disposal; disposal facility
   [dɪ'spəʊzl]
disposal: at sb's ~
   [ət dɪ'spəʊzl]
to dispose of sth
   [dɪ'spəʊz əv]
to disrupt [dɪs'rʌpt]
to distribute [dɪ'strɪbjuːt]
distribution; distribution
   network [ˌdɪstrɪ'bjuːʃn]
district heating
   ['dɪstrɪkt hiːtɪŋ]
division [dɪ'vɪʒn]
to draft [drɑːft]
to draw up [ˌdrɔː 'ʌp]
drawback ['drɔːbæk]
due: to be ~ to sth
   [bi 'djuː tə]
due diligence
   [djuː 'dɪlɪdʒəns]

E early retirement
   [ˌɜːli rɪ'taɪəmənt]
economist [ɪ'kɒnəmɪst]
economy [ɪ'kɒnəmi]
to educate ['edʒukeɪt]
educational [ˌedʒu'keɪʃənl]
effect: to come into ~
   [ˌkʌm ɪntuː ɪ'fekt]

	Translation			Translation

efficiency [ɪ'fɪʃnsi]
electrolysis [ɪˌlek'trɒləsɪs]
electrolyte [ɪ'lektrəlaɪt]
emission [ɪ'mɪʃn]
emissions trading
   [ɪ'mɪʃnz treɪdɪŋ]
to **emit** [ɪ'mɪt]
emitter [i'mɪtə]
to **encourage** [ɪn'kʌrɪdʒ]
energy-saving
   ['enədʒi seɪvɪŋ]
enforcement [ɪn'fɔːsmənt]
to **enhance** [ɪn'hɑːns]
to **enrich** [ɪn'rɪtʃ]
to **ensure** [ɪn'ʃʊə]
to **entail** [ɪn'teɪl]
entitled [ɪn'taɪtld]
entrant ['entrənt]
environment [ɪn'vaɪrənmənt]
environmentalist
   [ɪnˌvaɪrən'mentəlɪst]
to **envisage** [ɪn'vɪzɪdʒ]
equipment [ɪ'kwɪpmənt]
equity ['ekwəti]
essential [ɪ'senʃl]
to **establish** [ɪ'stæblɪʃ]
eventually [ɪ'ventʃuəli]
evidence ['evɪdəns]
exaggerated [ɪg'zædʒəreɪtɪd]
to **exceed** [ɪk'siːd]
exchange [ɪks'tʃeɪndʒ]
executive board
   [ɪg'zekjətɪv bɔːd]
to **expand** [ɪk'spænd]
expenditure [ɪk'spendɪtʃə]
expense [ɪk'spens]
expense: at sb's ~
   [ət ɪk'spens]
expertise [ˌekspə'tiːz]
to **explore** [ɪk'splɔː]
expropriation
   [eksˌprəupri'eɪʃn]
extract ['ekstrækt]
to **extract** [ɪk'strækt]
extraction [ɪk'strækʃn]

F **fabrication** [ˌfæbrɪ'keɪʃn]
to **face** [feɪs]
facility [fə'sɪləti]
failure ['feɪljə]
to **fall back** [ˌfɔːl 'bæk]
fallout ['fɔːlaʊt]
far-fetched [ˌfɑː 'fetʃt]
fault [fɔːlt]
fault: to be at ~ [bi ət 'fɔːlt]
to **favour** ['feɪvə]
favourable ['feɪvərəbl]
fee [fiː]
to **feed in** [ˌfiːd 'ɪn]
fissile ['fɪsaɪl]
fission ['fɪʃn]
to **fit with** ['fɪt wɪð]
fixed assets [fɪkst 'æsets]
flawed [flɔːd]

flow [fləʊ]
to **fluctuate** ['flʌktʃueɪt]
to **force** [fɔːs]
force majeure [ˌfɔːs mæ'ʒɜː]
forecast ['fɔːkɑːst]
forefront ['fɔːfrʌnt]
the former ['fɔːmə]
fossil fuel ['fɒsl fjuːəl]
framework ['freɪmwɜːk]
fuel ['fjuːəl]
fuel cell ['fjuːəl sel]
furthermore [ˌfɜːðə'mɔː]
to **fuse together**
   [ˌfjuːz tə'geðə]

G **gas-fired** [ˌgæs'faɪəd]
to **gather** ['gæðə]
to **gear: to be ~ed towards**
   sth [bi 'gɪəd təwɔːdz]
to **generate** ['dʒenəreɪt]
generation [ˌdʒenə'reɪʃn]
generator ['dʒenəreɪtə]
geothermal [ˌdʒiːəʊ'θɜːml]
to **get in touch** [get ɪn 'tʌtʃ]
giant ['dʒaɪənt]
glance [glɑːns]
global warming
   [ˌgləʊbl 'wɔːmɪŋ]
glut [glʌt]
to **go down** [ˌgəʊ 'daʊn]
grateful ['greɪtfl]
green tax [griːn 'tæks]
greenhouse gas
   [ˌgriːnhaʊs 'gæs]
grid [grɪd]

H **(hard) coal** [hɑːd 'kəʊl]
harmful ['hɑːmfl]
to **harness** ['hɑːnɪs]
harsh [hɑːʃ]
to **head** [hed]
to **head for** ['hed fə]
headquarters [ˌhed'kwɔːtəz]
heat [hiːt]
helpline ['helplaɪn]
to **hestitate** ['hezɪteɪt]
high-street spending
   [ˌhaɪstriːt 'spendɪŋ]
high-voltage
   [ˌhaɪ 'vəʊltɪdʒ]
to **highlight** ['haɪlaɪt]
hike [haɪk]
to **hit** [hɪt]
to **hold** [həʊld]
human resources
   [ˌhjuːmən rɪ'sɔːsɪz]
hydro ['haɪdrəʊ]
hydrocarbon
   [ˌhaɪdrəʊ'kɑːbən]
hydrogen ['haɪdrədʒən]

I to **illuminate** [ɪ'luːmɪneɪt]
to **illustrate** ['ɪləstreɪt]
impact ['ɪmpækt]

Translation

Translation

to **impair** [ɪm'peə]
impartial [ɪm'pɑːʃl]
to **implement** ['ɪmplɪmənt]
to **imply** [ɪm'plaɪ]
incentive [ɪn'sentɪv]
to **indicate** ['ɪndɪkeɪt]
indication [,ɪndɪ'keɪʃn]
induction [ɪn'dʌkʃn]
inefficiency [,ɪnɪ'fɪʃnsi]
inevitably [ɪn'evɪtəbli]
to **infringe** [ɪn'frɪndʒ]
innovation [,ɪnə'veɪʃn]
to **insist on** [ɪn'sɪst ɒn]
to **install** [ɪn'stɔːl]
installed capacity
    [ɪn,stɔːld kə'pæsəti]
insurance [ɪn'ʃʊərəns]
intelligence [ɪn'telɪdʒəns]
intention [ɪn'tenʃn]
interconnected
    [,ɪntəkə'nektɪd]
interconnector
    ['ɪntəkənektə]
interdepartmental
    [,ɪntə,diːpɑːt'mentl]
interim ['ɪntərɪm]
intermediate [,ɪntə'miːdiət]
to **interrupt** [,ɪntə'rʌpt]
intervention [,ɪntə'venʃn]
intriguing [ɪn'triːgɪŋ]
inventory ['ɪnvəntri]
investigation [ɪn,vestɪ'geɪʃn]
investment [ɪn'vestmənt]
ion ['aɪən]
IT (information technology)
    [,aɪ 'tiː / ɪnfə'meɪʃn
    tek'nɒlədʒi]

J to **jeopardize** ['dʒepədaɪz]
to **justify** ['dʒʌstɪfaɪ]

K **key account manager**
    [,kiː ə'kaʊnt mænɪdʒə]
to **kick off** [,kɪk 'ɒf]

L **labour** ['leɪbə]
to **lack** [læk]
latter ['lætə]
to **lay off** [,leɪ 'ɒf]
to **lead to** ['liːd tə]
to **leak** [liːk]
legislation [,ledʒɪs'leɪʃn]
level ['levl]
to **level off** [,levl 'ɒf]
liabilities [,laɪə'bɪlətiz]
liability [,laɪə'bɪləti]
lignite ['lɪgnaɪt]
lignite-fired [,lɪgnaɪt'faɪəd]
limelight ['laɪmlaɪt]
limit ['lɪmɪt]
to **link** [lɪŋk]
liquefied ['lɪkwɪfaɪd]
livelihood ['laɪvlihʊd]
LNG [,el en 'dʒiː]

load [ləʊd]
to **lobby** ['lɒbi]
location [ləʊ'keɪʃn]
long-distance [,lɒŋ 'dɪstəns]
loss [lɒs]
loyalty card ['lɔɪəlti kɑːd]

M **management** ['mænɪdʒmənt]
mandatory ['mændətəri]
measure ['meʒə]
to **mention** ['menʃn]
merger ['mɜːdʒə]
meter reading
    ['miːtə riːdɪŋ]
mine [maɪn]
minutes ['mɪnɪts]
to **mislead** [,mɪs'liːd]
missing ['mɪsɪŋ]
mockery; to make a
    mockery of sth
    [meɪk ə 'mɒkəri: əv]
momentum [mə'mentəm]
to **monitor** ['mɒnɪtə]
morale [mə'rɑːl]
moreover [mɔːr'əʊvə]
municipal [mjuː'nɪsɪpl]
municipality
    [mjuː,nɪsɪ'pæləti]

N to **name and shame**
    [,neɪm ənd 'ʃeɪm]
nationalization
    [,næʃnəlaɪ'zeɪʃn]
network ['netwɜːk]
nevertheless [,nevəðə'les]
nightmare ['naɪtmeə]
nitrogen oxide
    [,naɪtrədʒən 'ɒksaɪd]
non-discriminatory
    [,nɒndɪ'skrɪmɪnətəri]
non-related [,nɒn rɪ'leɪtɪd]
notably ['nəʊtəbli]
to **notify** ['nəʊtɪfaɪ]
nuclear ['njuːkliə]

O **objective** [əb'dʒektɪv]
objection [əb'dʒekʃn]
obliged: to be ~
    [bi ə'blaɪdʒd]
to **observe** [əb'zɜːv]
obstacle ['ɒbstəkl]
to **obtain** [əb'teɪn]
to **occur** [ə'kɜː]
offending [ə'fendɪŋ]
opencast ['əʊpənkɑːst]
to **operate** ['ɒpəreɪt]
operation [,ɒpə'reɪʃn]
operator ['ɒpəreɪtə]
opponent [ə'pəʊnənt]
ore [ɔː]
out of action [aʊt əv 'ækʃn]
outage ['aʊtɪdʒ]
to **outline** ['aʊtlaɪn]
overall [,əʊvər'ɔːl]

Translation

overhead line
['əʊvəhed laɪn]
overview ['əʊvəvju:]
oxygen ['ɒksɪdʒən]
ozone layer ['əʊzəʊn leɪə]

P participant [pɑ:'tɪsɪpənt]
particularly [pə'tɪkjələli]
payable; accounts payable
['peɪəbl]
payroll ['peɪrəʊl]
to peak [pi:k]
peak-load ['pi:kləʊd]
pellets ['pelɪts]
to penetrate ['penɪtreɪt]
pension ['penʃn]
perception [pə'sepʃn]
performance [pə'fɔ:məns]
period ['pɪəriəd]
personnel [,pɜ:sə'nel]
to phase out [,feɪz 'aʊt]
photovoltaic
[,fəʊtəʊvɒl'teɪɪk]
to pick up [,pɪk 'ʌp]
pie chart ['paɪ tʃɑ:t]
player ['pleɪə]
plentiful ['plentɪfl]
point of contact
[,pɔɪnt əv 'kɒntækt]
to point out [,pɔɪnt 'aʊt]
pointless ['pɔɪntləs]
pollution [pə'lu:ʃn]
to pool [pu:l]
to pose [pəʊz]
potential [pə'tenʃl]
powder ['paʊdə]
power ['paʊə]
power cut ['paʊə kʌt]
power plant ['paʊə plɑ:nt]
practical ['præktɪkl]
precisely [prɪ'saɪsli]
predicament [prɪ'dɪkəmnt]
pressure ['preʃə]
pressurized ['preʃəraɪzd]
to prevent [prɪ'vent]
proactive [,prəʊ'æktɪv]
process ['prəʊses]
to procure [prə'kjʊə]
procurement [prə'kjʊəmənt]
profit ['prɒfɪt]
profitable ['prɒfɪtəbl]
projection [prə'dʒekʃn]
to promote [prə'məʊt]
prompt [prɒmpt]
proportion [prə'pɔ:ʃn]
proposal [prə'pəʊzl]
to propose [prə'pəʊz]
pros and cons
[,prəʊz ənd 'kɒnz]
to protect [prə'tekt]
protocol ['prəʊtəkɒl]
to provide [prə'vaɪd]
provision [prə'vɪʒn]
proximity [prɒk'sɪməti]

Translation

public relations officer
[,pʌblɪk rɪ'leɪʃnz ɒfɪsə]
pulp [pʌlp]
pump-storage
[pʌmp 'stɔ:rɪdʒ]
purchase ['pɜ:tʃəs]
to purify ['pjʊərɪfaɪ]
to puzzle ['pʌzl]
pylon ['paɪlən]

Q quantity ['kwɒntəti]
to question ['kwestʃən]
questionable ['kwestʃənəbl]

R radiation [,reɪdi'eɪʃn]
to raise [reɪz]
range [reɪndʒ]
to rank [ræŋk]
rapidly ['ræpɪdli]
rapport [ræ'pɔ:]
to rate [reɪt]
to ratify ['rætɪfaɪ]
rating ['reɪtɪŋ]
ratio ['reɪʃiəʊ]
to reassure [,ri:ə'ʃʊə]
receivable; accounts
receivable [rɪ'si:vəbl]
recommendation
[,rekəmen'deɪʃn]
to recover [rɪ'kʌvə]
to rectify ['rektɪfaɪ]
red tape [,red 'teɪp]
redundancy [rɪ'dʌndənsi]
regulator ['regjuleɪtə]
relevant ['reləvənt]
reliability [rɪ,laɪə'bɪləti]
reliable [rɪ'laɪəbl]
to remain [rɪ'meɪn]
to remedy ['remədi]
remote [rɪ'məʊt]
renewable [rɪ'nju:əbl]
renewables [rɪ'nju:əblz]
repercussion [,ri:pə'kʌʃn]
repetition [,repə'tɪʃn]
to replace [rɪ'pleɪs]
to reprocess [,ri:'prəʊses]
reputation [,repju'teɪʃn]
request [rɪ'kwest]
requirement [rɪ'kwaɪəmənt]
research and development
[rɪ,sɜ:tʃ ən dɪ'veləpmənt]
reservation [,rezə'veɪʃn]
reserve [rɪ'zɜ:v]
reservoir ['rezəvwɑ:]
residential [,rezɪ'denʃl]
resistance [rɪ'zɪstəns]
to resolve [rɪ'zɒlv]
responsible: to be ~ for
[bi rɪ'spɒnsəbl fə]
restriction [rɪ'strɪkʃn]
to result in [rɪ'zʌlt ɪn]
retail ['ri:teɪl]
to retain [rɪ'teɪn]
to retrofit ['retrəʊfɪt]

Translation

Translation

return on investment
  [rɪˌtɜːn ɒn ɪnˈvestmənt]
to **reverse** [rɪˈvɜːs]
rod [rɒd]
room for improvement
  [ˌruːm fər_ɪmˈpruːvmənt]
rules and regulations
  [ˌruːlz ənd regjuˈleɪʃnz]
run-of-river [ˌrʌn əv ˈrɪvə]
rundown [ˈrʌndaʊn]

S to **safeguard** [ˈseɪfɡɑːd]
to **satisfy** [ˈsætɪsfaɪ]
scale [skeɪl]
scheme [skiːm]
sea level [ˈsiː levl]
to **seal** [siːl]
to **sell off** [ˌsel ˈɒf]
seriously [ˈsɪəriəsli]
set-up [ˈsetʌp]
severe(ly) [sɪˈvɪəli]
shareholder [ˈʃeəhəʊldə]
to **shift** [ˈʃɪft]
to **ship** [ʃɪp]
shortage [ˈʃɔːtɪdʒ]
signatory [ˈsɪɡnətri]
site [saɪt]
slide [slaɪd]
to **soar** [sɔː]
sober [ˈsəʊbə]
solar [ˈsəʊlə]
solid [ˈsɒlɪd]
to **solve** [sɒlv]
somewhat [ˈsʌmwɒt]
source [sɔːs]
to **speak for** [ˈspiːk fə]
specific [spəˈsɪfɪk]
spending [ˈspendɪŋ]
spent [spent]
sponsorship [ˈspɒnsəʃɪp]
spot price [ˈspɒt praɪs]
stable [ˈsteɪbl]
stack [stæk]
stakeholder [ˈsteɪkhəʊldə]
to **standardize** [ˈstændədaɪz]
state of affairs
  [ˌsteɪt əv əˈfeəz]
state-of-the-art
  [ˌsteɪt əv ði ˈɑːt]
statement [ˈsteɪtmənt]
steadily [ˈstedɪli]
steam [stiːm]
steeply [ˈstiːpli]
to **stick to sth** [ˈstɪk tə]
to **stifle** [ˈstaɪfl]
stock [stɒk]
storage [ˈstɔːrɪdʒ]
straightaway [ˌstreɪtəˈweɪ]
straightforward
  [ˌstreɪtˈfɔːwəd]
to **stress** [stres]
to **stretch** [stretʃ]
subsequent [ˈsʌbsɪkwənt]
subsidiary [səbˈsɪdiəri]

subsidy [ˈsʌbsədi]
substance [ˈsʌbstəns]
substation [ˈsʌbsteɪʃn]
sufficient [səˈfɪʃnt]
sulphur dioxide
  [ˌsʌlfə daɪˈɒksaɪd]
sunlight [ˈsʌnlaɪt]
superconductor
  [ˈsuːpəkəndʌktə]
supervisory [ˌsuːpəˈvaɪzəri]
supplier [səˈplaɪə]
to **supply** [səˈplaɪ]
surrounding [səˈraʊndɪŋ]
sustainable [səˈsteɪnəbl]
to **swallow up** [ˌswɒləʊ ˈʌp]
synchronous [ˈsɪŋkrənəs]

T to **tackle** [ˈtækl]
to **take apart**
  [ˌteɪk əˈpɑːt]
takeover [ˈteɪkəʊvə]
tantamount: to be ~ to sth
  [bi ˈtæntəmaʊnt tə]
target [ˈtɑːɡɪt]
task [tɑːsk]
temporary [ˈtemprəri]
terms [tɜːmz]
thermal [ˈθɜːml]
third-party; third-party
  access [ˌθɜːd ˈpɑːti]
thought-provoking
  [ˈθɔːt prəvəʊkɪŋ]
threat [θret]
through the backdoor
  [θruː ðə ˌbækˈdɔː]
tidal [ˈtaɪdl]
time: for the ~ being
  [fə ðə ˌtaɪm ˈbiːɪŋ]
track record [ˈtræk rekɔːd]
trade union [ˌtreɪd ˈjuːniən]
transformer [trænsˈfɔːmə]
transmission [trænsˈmɪʃn]
to **transmit** [trænsˈmɪt]
transparency [trænsˈpærənsi]
to **tread carefully**
  [ˌtred ˈkeəfəli]
treaty [ˈtriːti]
to **trigger** [ˈtrɪɡə]
turnover [ˈtɜːnəʊvə]

U **unaffected** [ˌʌnəˈfektɪd]
to **unbundle** [ʌnˈbʌndl]
uncertainty [ʌnˈsɜːtnti]
to **underestimate**
  [ˌʌndərˈestɪmeɪt]
unit [ˈjuːnɪt]
universe [ˈjuːnɪvɜːs]
unlike [ʌnˈlaɪk]
unstable [ʌnˈsteɪbl]
to **upgrade** [ˌʌpˈɡreɪd]
uphill [ˌʌpˈhɪl]
upsurge [ˈʌpsɜːdʒ]
upswing [ˈʌpswɪŋ]
uranium [juˈreɪniəm]

Translation

urgent ['ɜːdʒənt]
utility [juː'tɪləti]
to **utilize** ['juːtəlaɪz]
utmost ['ʌtməʊst]

V value ['væljuː]
vehicle ['viːəkl]
to **verify** ['verɪfaɪ]
versatile ['vɜːsətaɪl]
vertical ['vɜːtɪkl]
vessel ['vesl]
viable ['vaɪəbl]
vicinity: in the ~
[ɪn ðə və'sɪnəti]
to **view** [vjuː]
vitrify ['vɪtrɪfaɪ]
volatile ['vɒlətaɪl]
voltage ['vəʊltɪdʒ]
volume ['vɒljuːm]
voluntary ['vɒləntri]

W waste [weɪst]
watchdog ['wɒtʃdɒg]
water pipe ['wɔːtə paɪp]
whereby [weə'baɪ]
whim [wɪm]
wholesale ['həʊlseɪl]
wind farm ['wɪnd fɑːm]
worrying ['wʌriɪŋ]

Y yardstick ['jɑːdstɪk]

Glossary

balance sheet
A financial statement listing the value of assets, equity and liabilities of a company at a particular date.

base load
The minimum amount of electricity delivered and required over a specific period.

capacity
The maximum amount of electricity that can be generated from a power station or set of power stations.

collusion
Secret and improper talks between two or more companies, usually to fix prices.

commodity
Any product such as gas or electricity which can be bought or sold.

condenser
An apparatus which turns steam into water.

connection
Equipment which links a building with the local electricity or gas network.

cooling tower
A large circular structure at a power plant through which water is circulated to reduce its temperature.

core business
The main field of activities or operations of a company.

current assets
Things of value to a company which it uses in its normal day-to-day operations such as cash and materials.

decentralized energy system
Equipment which produces power for a nearby house, building or small community without the need for long-distance transportation of electricity.

denox plant
An apparatus at a power station which breaks down nitrogen oxides.

desulphurization plant
An apparatus at a power plant which removes sulphur oxides.

disinvestment
The withdrawal or reduction of capital investment.

distribution
The local transportation of electricity or gas from the main network to the final user.

district heating
A system for distributing heat, produced in a centralized plant, to homes and offices.

due diligence
A careful investigation of the financial and business situation of a company which may be taken over.

efficiency
A ratio between the output of a power station and the energy input, usually expressed as a percentage.

emissions trading
A system of buying and selling credits or allowances regarding CO_2 quotas in order to reduce the overall amount of pollution.

energy mix
The combination and proportions of primary fuels and sources used for electricity production.

expropriation
The taking of property from a private owner by the state or government, usually through compulsory purchase.

fixed asset
An object such as a building or power plant owned and utilized by a company for long-term use; it is not expected to be turned into cash.

flue gas
Exhaust gases such as sulphur oxides, nitrogen oxides and carbon dioxide which are produced in the combustion process at a power plant.

force majeure
An unavoidable event over which the parties who have signed a contract have no influence, e.g. bad weather conditions or a strike.

fossil fuel
Hydrocarbons such as gas, oil or coal used for producing electricity.

fuel cell
An apparatus which produces electrical current from a reaction between hydrogen and oxygen.

generation
The production of electrical power.

global warming
An increase in the average temperatures of the earth's atmosphere.

greenhouse gas
A gas such as CO_2 which causes the warming of the earth's atmosphere through its absorption of solar radiation.

grid
A network of pipelines, cables or overhead lines.

hydrogen economy
A concept for the future in which fossil fuels are replaced by hydrogen gas for energy production and industrial activities.

industrial customer
A company that buys and uses electricity or gas for manufacturing.

interim storage
A facility for holding (nuclear) waste for a limited period before it is moved to a final location.

intermediate/medium load
The amount of electricity delivered and required over a specific period between base and peak loads.

key account manager
A member of sales staff who looks after a specific group of customers.

legislation
Laws, or the act of making them.

lobbyist
A person who acts for an organization and tries to influence politicians or other national decision-makers.

municipal utility
A company owned by a city or town which transmits, distributes and delivers electricity and/or gas.

nationalization
The act of bringing a company under state ownership and control.

nuclear fission
A reaction in which nuclei of atoms split to release massive amounts of energy; uranium is the fuel used in this process.

nuclear fusion
A reaction in which nuclei of atoms fuse together to release massive amounts of energy.

peak load
The maximum amount of electricity delivered and required over a specific period.

power plant/station
A complex of buildings, machinery and equipment used for generating electricity.

profit and loss account
A financial statement of a company which shows its expenditures and income over a period; these are balanced to show a final profit or loss.

provisions
The money a company sets aside for future risk or use such as company pensions or the decommissioning of power plants.

pylon
A tall metal structure which carries an overhead line.

red tape
Another term for bureaucracy.

regulator
Organization or person who monitors and, if necessary, sanctions energy companies.

renewables
Primary energy sources such as wind, sun and water.

reprocessing plant
A facility in which nuclear waste is treated and processed.

residential/retail customer
A consumer who procures gas or electricity for home use.

retail price
The amount of money charged to the final user by energy companies for gas or electricity.

return on investment
The income that can be expected from an investment, usually expressed as a percentage.

spent fuel
Uranium that has been used up.

stack
A tall chimney at a power plant.

subsidiary
A company which belongs to a parent or holding company.

subsidy
Financial support for companies in an industry given by the government or state.

supply
The provision of gas or electricity to the final customer.

synergy
Combined advantages arising from the interaction of the companies involved in a merger or takeover.

transformer
Equipment which changes voltage levels of electricity.

transmission
The transport of electricity over long distances at high voltage.

transmission tower
A tall metal structure which carries overhead lines.

turbine
Equipment with a rotor which is driven by a jet of steam.

utility
A company which transmits, distributes and delivers electricity and/or gas.

waste disposal
The transporting, processing and recycling of unwanted substances.

watchdog
An organization working in the interests of customers which monitors the activities of energy companies, particularly regarding price.

wholesale price
The amount of money charged to companies which buy large volumes of gas or electricity; these companies then sell these commodities to the final customer.

Useful phrases and vocabulary

EXPRESSING OPINIONS AND (DIS)AGREEMENT

Giving your opinion
I think/feel (that) ...
In my opinion ...
In my view ...

Agreeing
Quite right.
That's true.
I quite agree.

Clarifying
So you're saying ...
You mean ...
What do you mean by ...?

Disagreeing
Actually, I think ...
To be honest ...
I don't quite agree.

DISCUSSING IN A MEETING

Proposing
Couldn't we just ...?
What if we ...?
Why don't we ...?

Asking for agreement/disagreement
Do we all agree on that?
Does anybody object to this?
Who's in favour of this proposal?

Showing concern
I have some reservations/concerns about ...
Actually, I don't think that's a good idea.

Emphasizing
I'd again like to point out that ...
I know I keep going on about this, but ...

CHAIRING A MEETING

Opening the meeting
Can we now agree on the overall procedure?
First of all, I think we should establish the overall procedure.
The main objectives of the meeting are ...
Does that seem acceptable to you?

Asking somebody to start
Would you like to start, John?
John, would you like to kick off?

Keeping to the agenda
OK, could we please come back to the agenda?
I'm afraid that's not part of the discussion.

Asking for clarification
I don't quite follow. What do you mean by ...?
I don't really get what you mean.

GIVING A PRESENTATION

Opening
Let me first introduce myself.
I'm/My name is ...
In this talk I want/would like to ...
I'll begin by (+ -ing form of verb).
I'm going to be covering ...
Let's start with (+ noun).

Introducing other factors or points
If I could now turn to ...
Now, turning to ...
Let me move on to ...

Introducing graphs and diagrams
I'd like you to look at this graph/diagram/(pie) chart/
  transparency/slide.
This graph shows ...
You can see here that ...

Comparing factors
First of all ...
Firstly ..., secondly ..., thirdly ...
On the one hand ... , on the other hand ...

Questions
Please don't hesitate to interrupt me if you have any
  questions.
If you have any questions, I'll be pleased to answer
  them at the end.

Finishing
That completes my overview (of ...).
So, to summarize/sum up ...
Thank you for your attention.

DESCRIBING TRENDS

It grew/rose/increased/picked up/recovered/peaked.
It fell/declined/hit a low.
It fluctuated/was volatile.
It remained stable.
This happened/occurred because ...
We expected this change, but ...
Although there was a fall/rise ...
This was due to ...
This was because of ...

DESCRIBING A PROCESS

Firstly/First of all ...
After that ...
The next step/stage is ...
Then ...

Following that ...
Finally ...
The final step ...

TELEPHONING FOR INFORMATION

Introductions
Hello … . This is … speaking.
Hi …, it's … here.

Asking for information
I need some information about …
I'd like to have some (more) information about …
Can/Could you give me more information about …?
Can/Could you please tell me (about) …?
Who/What/When/Where/Why/How …?
What about …?

Asking for repetition
Sorry, I didn't quite catch that.
Would you mind repeating that?

Positive response
Sure.
No problem.
I'd be happy to.

Negative response
I'm afraid I can't help you there.
I'm afraid not.

REPLYING TO INVITATIONS

Accepting
I was delighted to receive your kind invitation …
Thank you very much for your kind invitation to take part in …
I would very much like to attend.

Making requests
Would/Could you please …?
I would be grateful if you could …
I would appreciate it if you could …

DEALING WITH COMPLAINTS

Reassuring
We are taking this matter very seriously.
I can/would also like to assure you that …
We are making every effort to …
We are doing our utmost/all we can to …

Not accepting responsibility
I fully understand your concern but …
I would like to stress that …
These are circumstances beyond our control.
Nevertheless, …
That's quite impossible.

USEFUL VERBS (IN CONTEXT)

Your language

to commission	This power plant **was commissioned** last year.	
to comply with	Energy companies have to **comply with** all rules and regulations.	
to condense	Steam **condenses** into water at the power station.	
to convert	DC **is converted** into AC if necessary.	
to decommission	Some plants **were decommissioned** as they were not economic.	
to deplete	Coal stocks **have been depleted** due to a rise in consumption.	
to disinvest	Unwanted activities **will be disinvested**.	
to dismantle	A nuclear plant has to **be dismantled** at the end of its life.	
to dispose of	Some companies **dispose of** waste by burning it.	
to distribute	Gas **is distributed** throughout Europe from fields in the North Sea.	
to emit	Many harmful gases **are emitted** from power stations.	
to exceed	Emissions must not **exceed** certain levels.	
to fluctuate	Wholesale prices **have been fluctuating** over the past year.	
to generate	Electricity **is generated** at our power stations.	
to lay off	Many employees **were laid off** after the takeover.	
to liberalize	Customers can choose their supplier as the market **is liberalized**.	
to merge	Two utilities **have merged** to form a new company.	
to monitor	Our image in the media **is being monitored** by management.	
to operate	The TSO **operates** the transmission grid.	
to phase out	Some countries wish to **phase out** nuclear power.	
to pollute	Generators that **pollute** too much must buy credits or allowances.	
to procure	Our company **procures** large quantities of gas.	
to regulate	Some countries **regulate** the energy market through price controls.	
to reprocess	Nuclear waste **is reprocessed** before final storage.	
to retrofit	Our older plants **have been retrofitted** to bring them up to standard.	
to subsidize	The coal industry **is subsidized** through state support.	
to supply	We **supply** gas to a number of different companies.	
to switch	Many residential customers **switched** suppliers because of high prices.	
to transmit	Electricity **is transmitted** through the grid.	

Abbreviations, acronyms, and numbers

Abbreviations and acronyms

ACER	Agency for the Co-ordination of Energy Regulators
AEP	Association of Energy Producers
AC	alternating current
CCGT	combined cycle gas turbine
CCPP	combined cycle power plant
CCT	clean coal technology
CEO	chief executive officer
CFO	chief financial officer
CHP	combined heat and power
CO	carbon monoxide
CO_2	carbon dioxide
DC	direct current
dept	department
DSO	distribution systems operator
EASEE	European Association for the Streamlining of Energy Exchange
EC	European Commission
EEX	European Energy Exchange
EU	European Union
GHG	greenhouse gas
GPA	Gas Producers Association
H	hydrogen
IAEA	International Atomic Energy Authority
IAHE	International Association for Hydrogen Energy
IEA	International Energy Agency
IGCC	integrated gasification combined cycle
Inc	incorporated
IPP	independent power producer
ISO	independent systems operator, International Standards Organization
ITER	International Thermonuclear Experimental Reactor
LNG	liquefied natural gas
Ltd	limited
misc	miscellaneous
NOx	nitrogen oxides
NGO	non-governmental organization
O_2	oxygen
OECD	Organization for Economic Co-operation and Development
PLC	public limited company
p.a.	per annum
PV	photovoltaic
Q	quarterly
RAPS	remote area power supply
REEF	Renewable Energy Equity Fund
SO_2	sulphur dioxide
TSO	transmission systems operator
UCTE	Union for the Co-ordination of Transmission of Electricity
UNEP	United Nations Environment Programme
WCI	World Coal Institute
WTO	World Trade Organization

A	amperes
bbl	barrel
bn	billion (1 000 000 000)
°C	degrees Celsius (centigrade)
GW	gigawatt
Ha	hectare
Hz	hertz
J	joule
kW	kilowatt
kWh	kilowatt-hour
l	litre
m	million (1 000 000)
m	metre
m^3	cubic metres
m^2	square metres
MW	megawatt
t	ton
TCE	tons of coal equivalent
TW	terawatt
V	volt, voltage
W	watt
Ω	ohm

Numbers

356	three hundred (and) fifty-six
1,356	one thousand three hundred (and) fifty-six
1,256,349	one million two hundred (and) fifty-six thousand three hundred (and) forty-nine
1.356	one **point** three five six
1.035	one **point zero/nought** three five

mega	1 000 000	10^6	ten to the power of six
giga	1 000 000 000	10^9	ten to the power of nine
tera	1 000 000 000 000	10^{12}	ten to the power of twelve

Money

€1,356.59	one thousand three hundred (and) fifty-six euro**s** fifty-nine
$10 m	ten million dollar**s**
¥10 bn	ten billion yen

Years

2000	two thousand
2009	two thousand and nine
2010	twenty ten
2015	twenty fifteen
2020	twenty twenty